EX

MOUNT MARY COLLEGE

Luther Burbank

THE
Riverside Library

The Harvest of the Years

By

LUTHER BURBANK

WITH

WILBUR HALL

WITH ILLUSTRATIONS

BOSTON AND NEW YORK
HOUGHTON MIFFLIN COMPANY
The Riverside Press Cambridge

The Riverside Press

CAMBRIDGE · MASSACHUSETTS

PRINTED IN THE U.S.A.

WHEN we no longer look at an organic being as a savage looks at a ship, as something wholly beyond his comprehension; when we regard every production of nature as one which has had a long history; when we contemplate every complex structure and instinct as the summing up of many contrivances, each useful to the possessor, in the same way as any great mechanical invention is the summing up of the labor, the experience, the reason, and even the blunders of numerous workmen; — when we thus view each organic being, how far more interesting — I speak from experience — does the study of natural history become!

CHARLES DARWIN

LUTHER BURBANK — NATURALIST

By Wilbur Hall

Luther Burbank was past sixty before he could find the time he desired for the making of exact records of his innumerable and unique experiments with plants; he was seventy before the itch that had always been on him to express on paper his thoughts, reactions, observations, and philosophies could be even in slight measure gratified.

Unquestionably if he had lived he would have poured forth his naturalist's soul, and the last years would have been productive of exhilarating, pungent, and enlightening essays and books that would have greatly enriched our literature of thought and comment.

What is saved of all the treasure he had stored happens to be this volume.

He wrote, and left behind him, first and last, more than a million words concerning his intimate friendships with plants, but what he felt and thought, what he aspired to and how much he achieved, the things he saw in life and learned from experience, what disappointments were his and what triumphs — the true picture of the gallant, lovable, kindly, shrewd, whimsical Luther Burbank will never be limned, in his own words, except in these pages.

That it was I who came to this rare opportunity resulted on the mere accident of my writing habitually in the vernacular in which Luther Burbank thought.

Working with him on a briefer and more prosy volume, I was interrupted by the little Big Chief a dozen times an hour with some surprised, characteristic ejaculation.

'When did I tell you that?'

'How did you happen to put that in?'

'That isn't what I said — but that's the way I would have said it!'

It developed, presently, that my natural idiom was so like his own that he himself could not say where something he had written left off and something I was quoting or filling in began.

This delighted him out of all proportion. 'He does all the work!' he would exclaim, whimsically. 'He grinds away — grinds away — getting a hot-box on that old typewriter, and out pops a book in my very words!' And he would laugh and rub his hands and make innocent bystanders listen to selections from the manuscript. He was like a boy with a mechanical monkey that will climb a string!

For a very practical and utilitarian purpose Luther Burbank had dictated, at one time and another, an amazing mass of material concerning his methods, technique, experiments, and scientific discoveries in the world of plants. Browsing through this heavy pasturage with one eye open for cowslips I came frequently on paragraphs having nothing to do — or nothing immediate — with the subject-matter, but that gave me, in flashing glimpses, a vague picture of the real mind and soul of the man. I had thought of him as a 'wizard of plant life' — as what Hugo de Vries, the Dutch botanist, called him: 'A gardener touched with genius.' I began to see him as a cosmopolite and polished man of the world, as a philosopher, as a naturalist in love with Nature and life, as a humanist at once keenly interested in man and penetrating and exact in his judgments of men. I began to realize him as an extraordinary and versatile thinker. I began to appraise him as copy!

He fell in with the project for this book with ready enthusiasm.

'Folks wonder how I've kept so young,' he said, one day. 'I'm almost seventy-seven and I can still go over a gate or run a foot-race or kick the chandelier. That's because my body is no older than my mind — and my mind is adolescent. It has never grown up. It never will, I hope. I'm as inquisitive as I was at eight.'

It was true. He could not pass a new house, a shop window, a patent washing machine, a ditch-digger, a strange plant, or a carpenter at work, without stopping to look or watch. He was always asking, 'What is this?' — and then, 'How does it work?'

This insatiable and consuming appetite of his for new information was the basis, of course, for his achievements in the plant world; more important for my purposes, it was the explanation of his incredible knowledge of life. What he knew was only the beginning of what he wanted to know. That is why his judgments were both profound and tolerant; he saw through men and events and movements and motives, but the incompleteness of all data caused him to stop short of conclusions. 'Up to now,' he was saying, 'we are what we are because of our heredities and our environments. But this is not the end. It may be only the beginning. I don't know what the end will be; no man knows anything that is final. Wait a while. Hold your horses!'

'These folks want you for the week-end,' he said once, to his beloved wife and play-fellow, Betty. 'You'll lug along a lot of dresses, you'll go to long dinners and be kept up till midnight, you'll make calls you don't want to and listen to bores and come home all tuckered out. You don't want to go down there at all. You don't want to bother.'

Then he stepped back, put his head on one side, and chuckled.

'Or do you?' he concluded.

The outline for this book absorbed him, though it was being made at his busiest season, when the press of other work on him was heavy and constant. He enjoyed every minute of it.

A phrase would give him an idea that would start him off on a half-hour's excursion into memory. A question would shoot him out of his chair, as though he had been propelled from a gun, and send him scurrying to his bookshelves or his manuscript files for a reference, a date, a name, or a fact. You would be in the midst of a knotty section and he would suddenly bolt, shouting over his shoulder: 'Come along: I've just thought of something!' And it would be a photograph, a clipping in an old scrap-book, or a letter that would fit right in and shed an effulgent and illuminating light on the murky corner.

He took huge delight in my own inquisitiveness, half a habit, half caught from him.

'Never saw such a fellow!' he exclaimed to Mrs. Burbank. 'Into everything — upstairs and down-stairs, cellar to garret. He trails me into the gardens, he doesn't know what bashfulness is; he pesters me night and day, and he asks questions I wouldn't answer from the grand jury!' He laughed. 'I never know where he'll be next — wouldn't be a bit surprised some night to turn back my covers and find him in my bed!'

He took a sly, impish delight in pretending that he wanted to get into this record some points that his wife wouldn't approve. He would hatch up the most scandalous schemes for revelations. He would whisper and wink and let on that we were in a deep conspiracy to circumvent her and publish appalling confessions.

When she left the room one day, he put a hand on my knee and jerked a thumb toward the door she had just passed through.

'She don't like this religious talk!' he whispered stagily. 'Don't like it at all. She was raised Advent! We'll have to be 'cute to get away with it!'

Then, when you almost began to take him seriously, he would tell her the whole joke — and laugh and laugh and laugh!

It was like collaborating with a vaudeville pro-gramme!

Underlying all his fun and whimsy and his ten-

dency toward an almost boisterous exuberance was
the tenderness of a mother and the sensitiveness of a
child. His humor was that poignant sort which is
akin to tears; just under his highest mood was a
serious, deep, understanding sympathy.

A dog, a child, a tramp, an ailing woman, an unfortunate, a crippled bird — even a broken blossom
on one of his own plants! — could move him to
great lengths of pity and generosity. Children loved
and understood him; he was the friend of all the
youngsters of the countryside. The needy actually
imposed on him. He had an unfailing instinct for
sham — but his heart usually played his head false
and made him give even to rascals and frauds.

His love and tenderness expressed themselves in
hyberbole.

Sitting around the table one night with his wife
and her little niece and ward, Betty Jane, and with
Bonita, his dog, half a whippet, half some short-
haired terrier of nameless lineage, Luther Burbank
took a large sheet of paper and on it drew a great
pyramid, a medium pyramid, and a smaller pyramid; then, in one far corner of the page, he drew a
regular picket fence of microscopic ones.

'That's what I've been trying to get at for
months,' he said, as though it were the working-
drawing of an epochal invention.

'It's very interesting,' Mrs. Burbank said. 'But
what does it mean?'

The Big Chief put his pencil point on the first
triangle.

'That is you,' he said sententiously. 'This one is
Betty Jane, and this is Bonita.' Then he touched

the inconsequential line off in the corner. He fairly brushed it aside. 'That's the rest of the world,' he said.

He loved extravagant expressions and descriptions, and employed them always except when they might be misunderstood or might deceive some one.

He never said: 'I have to keep in touch with my men.'

No; he would exclaim, excitedly: 'Land alive, those men can't work for more than a year without my dropping in once in a while and telling them what I want done!'

'There isn't a stamp in this house!' he said once. 'You would think somebody would buy stamps enough sometime, for a change!' He turned to his secretary. 'I wish you'd go down to the post-office and buy a thousand dollars' worth of two-cent stamps!'

If some one hadn't stopped her she would have obeyed that order. She was a single-minded and loyal soul!

'Well,' he would sigh, 'there's no use trying to make that fellow over, I suppose. But some day he'll grow to his hoe, leaning on it the way he does, and they'll both rust down together.'

'Photographers?' he cried. 'You'd think they'd made enough pictures of me, wouldn't you? I'll bet I've been snapped ten million times.'

Numbers meant little to him. He liked to roll large figures on his tongue.

'I guess I've met as many people as anybody that ever stayed home and tried to 'tend to business. They've come in hundreds of thousands.

And letters! There are eight thousand unanswered letters right there in that box, and every mail anywhere from two to five hundred more come in!'

But the moment he was talking of his work, his methods, his experiments, or his results, he was as coldly exact and meticulous as a chemist mixing high explosives. Finding him extravagant in his casual speech there were those who thought he might be extravagant in his reports, his assertions, or his claims. If they tried to test him they came out of the encounter with their fingers burned. He never made a mistake there!

The first project completed, the work on this book was begun, and for two months it went forward with Mr. Burbank ever a more enthusiastic and ever a more helpful and generous collaborator. He never tired of it, though he was often pitifully and tragically tired.

Early in the spring of 1926, repeating what he had been saying for forty years, though perhaps in different words, Luther Burbank precipitated a religious controversy that, with himself as storm center, swept the whole country and cast its light pretty well around the world.

He had grown increasingly impatient with bigotry and superstition as his own first-hand acquaintance with Nature and science had developed; the trial of a high-school teacher in a Southern State for the 'heresy' of teaching Darwin's evolution aroused him to a conviction that he ought to speak out, without mincing words, and declare for truth.

'People respect me,' he said, in discussing his programme. 'They know that I am honest and that I haven't an axe to grind. They like me because I like plants and they trust me because I have never misled them. I guess, if they know me at all, they know I'm a fairly decent, law-abiding, ethical sort of man, and what I say would carry weight with a lot of folks who wouldn't listen to others. The time has come for honest men to denounce false teachers and attack false gods.'

In a memorable address, in a San Francisco church, Luther Burbank declared to the world his belief in righteousness and the highest spiritual development and his utter unbelief in the mockery of dogma.

A whirlwind of hatred engulfed him within twenty-four hours, tempered only by fluent and admiring congratulations from thousands and thousands of the thoughtful. If he had contented himself with his message, this storm would not have affected him, for he had weathered several similar ones before and had come off unscathed. But he was misled into believing that logic, kindliness, and reason could convince and help the bigoted.

I was with him during those weeks almost constantly; I saw him growing tired and harassed, not by the dispute or the vilification heaped on him by the regenerate, but by the physical task entailed. He tried to reply to all the letters, using mild but fearless good sense with those who attacked him, and amplifying his original statement for those who supported him.

He fell sick. The sickness was fated to be his last. What killed Luther Burbank, at just that time

and in just that abrupt and tragic fashion, was his
baffled, yearning, desperate effort to make people
understand. His desire to help them, to clarify
their minds, and to induce them to substitute fact
for hysteria drove him beyond his strength. He
grew suddenly old attempting to make reasonable a
people which had been unreasonable through twenty
stiff-necked generations. His age, his long life of exacting physical labor, and his pitiful attempt to give
sight to the wilfully blind brought him to his bed.

He died, not a martyr to truth, but a victim of
the fatuity of blasting dogged falsehood.

No sunnier man ever lived than Luther Burbank.

It was one of his cherished illusions that he was
'an old growler.' He did growl. He growled in a
good-humored, whimsical, ludicrous fashion that de-
ceived no one. He growled mostly at himself, though
sometimes at people or about people who were 'de-
laying the game.' Never, though, did his growling
hurt or wound or really convince. It was one of his
games.

His laughter was ready and contagious. He could
not tell a funny story, though he often tried, and
would get more enjoyment out of his own inability
to approach the point with the delicate abruptness
of the born yarn-spinner than he could have got
from the best jest ever coined. What he could do was
to wring the neck of a proverb until it was funny, or
put a situation into a few excruciating phrases, or
twist an otherwise labored statement into a terse
and pungent epigram. Perhaps the best, but certainly one of his most characteristic epigrams was
the one, called forth when some well-meaning ac-

quaintances caused him a great deal of worry through ill-advised efforts in his behalf, that is to be found in this volume:

'I would rather have a dozen enemies than one fool friend!'

He skylarked like a boy, and his wife tells of evenings when she was driven to the sanctuary of her bedroom by the wild and boisterous hilarity of Big Chief and Betty Jane, her niece and ward. They would romp, roar, wrestle, dance, get laughing and roll on the floor; they were worse, Mrs. Burbank says, than a houseful of growing boys. Luther Burbank liked romps and laughter and physical expressions for his exuberance of spirit.

A fair joke on himself always found him a good audience, but he was sensitive about jokes made around or concerning his work. The stock jest, employed in a thousand forms, that made him the creator of absurd plants through the crossing of two — 'Luther Burbank crossed the eggplant and the milkweed to make an omelette plant' is one of the cruder and more familiar guises of this classification — left him a little cold. The slight innuendo, probably wholly unintentional on the part of the jesters, hurt the man whose every thought and activity was motivated by a transcendent love of plant life. One of his 'fool friends' sent him, on one occasion, a phonograph record of a monologue by a heavy-handed jokesmith on Luther Burbank and his marvelous creations in plant life; presumably it was funny, but Mr. Burbank winced when it was run. It was characteristic of him, though, that he would not destroy it.

Perhaps the reason may be guessed, by indirection, from this epigrammatic description he once gave of an important man who engaged in a newspaper controversy with nitwits. 'Too bad!' he said. 'He didn't accomplish anything except to bring a lot of nobodies into the limelight by answering them.'

Merry, humorous, whimsical, loving life and loving laughter, Luther Burbank radiated a personality that drew toward him every one he encountered. Strangely enough this appeal he had for people attracted them even through correspondence or through the less immediate agency of the newspapers and magazines. Thousands who had never seen him felt affectionately toward him; after his death messages poured in for weeks, from all over the world and from all sorts and conditions of people, and almost without exception they wrote proudly that they had always respected, honored, and loved him.

What was this aura — this radiance — that communicated itself to men, women, and children everywhere? Luther Burbank wrote comparatively little for publication; his interviews in newspapers and magazines scarcely mirrored the man; true, hundreds of thousands saw pictures of him, printed or on the silver screen, but in this day when every one from champion sprinters to little princes in the throes of baptism is in the 'weeklies,' it seems remarkable that he was singled out of the ruck. The explanation that he loved and worked with the flowers that speak every language and to every age is scarcely adequate to explain the universal love called forth by this quiet little man.

Perhaps his own theory of life and the future contains the soundest explanation.

Luther Burbank believed neither in heaven nor in hell, in the transmigration of souls nor the translation of the body.

The ultimate doctrine in his creed was an unshaken faith in the Immortality of Influence.

For him 'the life everlasting' was a phrase — a figure of speech. He had as little curiosity about the unknowable as any man who ever lived, and considerably less concern with the future. For him life overflowed with wonder, beauty, delight, and the work he found committed to his hand, and whether anything was to go on for him or not interested him not a whit. Sufficient unto the day was the heaven thereof!

But he did know and confess an abiding faith in the everlasting and eternal and all-important power on the race, the world, the scheme of things — on all life — of influence. To his mind the influence shed by a bad man was that man's own reward and punishment; the influence of a good and pure and worthy life was pervasive and everliving. And there was a touch of the mystic about Luther Burbank. He actually realized that influence, good and bad, as a tangible, concrete, observable power in the world. He could feel the effect on his own life of the Judas Iscariots of time as perceptibly as of Jesus Christ; the eternal malevolence generated by tyrants, assassins, inquisitors, gunmen, and moral perverts was to him as potent for evil as the everlasting goodness and altruism of the Gautamas, the Saint Johns, the Constantines, the Emersons, the Clara

Bartons, and the Jacob Riises. You could not, he said, either thwart or kill the influence of human lives.

He lived in entire confidence that good work well done, sincere motives, and loyalty to high ideals formed the whole duty of man; to these he added, for the creation of a real heaven on earth, the single essential, Love. As far as in him lay he lived his creed; he died without in the slightest amending or altering it, and stories that, in the end, he recanted or turned to religious teachings or teachers for consolation or comfort are, at best, apocryphal; at worst, impudent falsehood.

No man, in death, ever presented a countenance more beautiful, peaceful, or serene. He was like a child asleep.

The hand falters and fails at an attempt to describe Luther Burbank clearly for those who never saw him, and for those who, having seen him for a moment or an hour, caught only a meager glimpse of him as he was.

Small, lithe, slightly stooped, with knees and elbows bent a little from long years of the hardest physical labor, Luther Burbank was yet so stamped with the 'outward symbols of an inward grace' as to stand out in any crowd as sharply as a lighthouse in a fog. Everywhere people recognized him as 'Somebody.' His personality flowed from him almost visibly.

He had a peculiar indifference to the looks of his clothes coupled with the most meticulous care as to their quality. The result was that, when he looked

most a tramp at a casual glance, close scrutiny iden-
tified him as well-dressed. In his gardens, no matter
how dirty, warm, or disheveled he became, he was
always more picturesque than he was ordinary; he
had a way of wearing his hat, pulling a muffler about
his neck, or slipping on gloves that gave him an indubitable air of gallantry and personableness. If he
had been a banker, he would have been famed as the
best-dressed man in town!

His energy, his enthusiasms, coupled with his
high spirit, combined to give him an almost boyish
appearance, despite his silvery-white hair and the
deep lines that experience and laughter and grief
had carved in his face. Sculptors said he had a perfect head. All his pictures show beauty, in the face
as well as in the set, shape, and size of his head. The
growth of his mind and soul registered itself on him:
if at forty he was a good-looking man, at seventy he
was strikingly and arrestingly beautiful. There is
no other word. He was never handsome.

His eyes were a deep and placid blue, and a little
roguish. On rare occasions they would darken and
narrow and snap — but he was angry seldom. When
he was he did not raise his voice. Occasionally he
would 'pound down' as Betty Jane, Mrs. Burbank's
niece and ward once said, when a man or an incident
tried his patience too far, but he was always calm.
He could use simple, chaste, elegant English words,
in a quiet tone of voice, without profanity or exple-
tives, and make a transgressor feel that a jail sentence would be a kindness compared to one of Luther Burbank's rebukes. . . . There were times when
his English was not so chaste. He had a profane

vocabulary; on rare occasions he unlimbered his big guns.

His movements were quick, accurate, efficient. His hands were supple and very strong: he had that deftness that marks all experts, whether a great batter, a swift telegraph operator, an old lady knitting, or a finished painter at his easel. He never made two motions where one would do; in picking up a pen he did it, instinctively, so that it was ready to lay to paper — and he always wrote with his pen between the index and second finger, supported by the thumb. When he was grafting or budding or pollenizing his hands were like dragonflies above a pool.

He clung to 'boiled shirts' to the end, only toying with more modern patterns, which he would buy extravagantly — and never wear. He had as many pairs of shoes as a leading lady, and gloves enough to start a store. And yet he was frugal in most things — not stingy, but habitually New England. His food was of the plainest, his tastes simple, his pleasures inexpensive ones. On his wife or little Betty, on tools or equipment for the Farms, on photographs for his bulletins, he spent money like water — had, in fact, to be watched and restrained. He was a queer admixture of a little, old-fashioned, careful Massachusetts bachelor, a gnome, a genius, a prankish boy, a spendthrift, and a temperamental artist. More exactly he had in him a little of all the most lovable and attractive and desirable traits of humankind — he was an epitome of the best of the race. Plus a modicum of something careless observers thought conceit. It was not egoistic complacence. It was a boundless pride in The Work. As the man who was doing that work, Luther Burbank thought considerably of Luther Burbank. As Luther Burbank, citizen, husband, friend, he did not rate Luther Burbank above any other law-abiding and peace-loving gentleman. Sometimes he was a little chagrined at the antics of the latter individual; apparently from his earlier years he was filled with amazement and delight at the achievements and triumphs of the former.

When I had finished the first writing, referred to on a previous page, and had read for Mr. Burbank's editing the last installment, I made a hasty farewell, because he was very tired and very much harassed by other cares and troubles. Mrs. Burbank says that the Big Chief, sitting in his glass-enclosed study on the south side of the rambling house where he lived, rose quickly, went to a window, and watched me down the path. Then he turned quickly — impulsively.

'Betty, call him back, will you?' he cried.

Mrs. Burbank, knowing that the work was, for the time being, done, hesitated.

'What's wrong, Big Chief?' she inquired. 'Do you really want him back?'

He shook his head slowly; sighed.

'Let it go,' he said. 'No, it's all right. Only he looks sort of lonesome!'

We laid Luther Burbank to rest under a cedar in the yard of the old homestead in which he lived for forty years and on the grounds of which he did most of his revolutionary and incalculably valuable work for his fellow man.

He used to go there, often, where the drooping limbs of the great tree sweep down to touch the earth and to form about the stalwart, friendly trunk a little quiet house of coolness and the sweet balsam of the needles. Sitting or lying on the ground, or playing there with Betty Jane, he would be utterly relaxed and at peace. He loved that cedar, and its shaded canopy of branches.

That is why he was laid there for his long rest.

There was nothing funereal or conventional about the feeling with which he was placed there, blanketed with flowers. All the grief felt was free of bitterness, all the tenderness was swept clean of vain regret. It was and is as though he were at peace — simply sleeping there, so near still, so dear still, so real still.

Only now and again, in the twilight that used to be his time for intimate talks and for some reading aloud, or when his lack and loss are brought abruptly to the mind, or when there is proposed some outing that would have found him eager and restive — first to be off! — only now and again, in moments when it seems that the Big Chief ought to be found laughing and unexpected in a door, or stretching out under his own, homely old rug on the battered sofa in his favorite room, or sitting relaxed, his sensitive fingers playing with Betty Jane's black hair or fondling Nita, the dog, those who knew him best and loved him most dearly find the tears springing, and with throats a little dry they look at one another as though they might well want to say:

'Call him back. He seems sort of lonesome!'

THE HARVEST OF THE YEARS

THE
HARVEST OF THE YEARS

I

BACK of every plant, every shellfish, every burrowing rodent or ravaging animal, and back of every human being, there stretches an illimitable and mysterious heredity, about the nature and influence of which scientists and the wise men spend their lives in research, speculation, and conclusions. Little as we know of this subject we have pretty generally agreed that the newborn child has a heritage of tendencies and inclinations which furnish the foundation or groundwork from which he must build his house of Life.

But it is only the foundation, I think; the superstructure is built by environment. Heredity is the shape of the edifice, its position on the ground, whether a hillside or a plain, a rugged rock or a piece of shifting sand; environment is the architect of the structure. Probably I have used that word 'environment' more often than any other man who ever lived; if I seem to put stress on it, as these papers grow, it is because seventy years of interest in plant life and of wholesale experimentation to discover, test, practice, and then codify the laws underlying that life have compelled me to the belief that environment is the great moulding force behind the steady upward progress of the universe.

My own heredity gave me a ground-plan for my life that called for an edifice sturdily built on the rock of knowledge and fact, and yet that was plastic enough to enable me to use a front elevation strangely like a house of dreams — a veritable Castle in Spain. Behind me was hard-headed practicality, shrewd Yankee thrift, and insistence on an exact basis for reasoning and planning. At the same time there came to me, in vein and nerve-system and brain-cell, the imagination, the tendency to dreaming dreams, and the instinct to create that impelled me to invention, to inquiry, and to the seeing of visions.

My father, Samuel Walton Burbank, was a New-Englander of pure and unmixed physical strain, but it was not the shallow soil, the rocky structure below, the hardness of labor, the rigor of the winters, and the austerity of the people about him that he saw; he was a man of imagination and a facile mind, and he loved beauty and the sunshine and pleasantness of the land, in its garments of spring and autumn, and was influenced by them. My mother was shrewd and practical, of a nervous temperament, quick and impulsive, yet kindly, intelligent, and with a great love of her garden. She had an unusual bent for making things grow, whether from domesticated seeds or from bulbs or cuttings or roots found in the woods all about; one of my earliest recollections is of the beauty and peace and fragrance of that old-fashioned garden of hers.

My birthplace was the brick house on the Burbank farm in Lancaster Township, near Boston, Massachusetts; I cannot but believe that its diversified nature and activities were strongly influential on my life. The farm work, the pottery kiln my grandfather built and that led to the foundation of a brickyard, the woodlots from which were taken the fuel supplies for house and kilns, gardens, berry-patches, the sugar bush, and other activities not only kept a small boy busy, but kept him interested, since there was never any long stretch of monotonous work — that murderer of enthusiasm and destroyer of the sheer fun of labor! Near by and all around us were manufacturing plants of the most diverse kinds, where, at that time, something of almost every fabricated article used in growing America was made.

Physically, too, the old Lancaster farm was a broad education to a boy full of curiosity and keen to put his nose into all sorts of businesses and natural wonders. Massachusetts was — and is still! — a good place in which to be born. I can remember now the keen sweetness of the air on sharp mornings, the sun on snow or on green carpets of grass on the rolling land, running up sharply, here and there, to hills where the ribs of the earth were revealed in rugged outcroppings of rock; I can hear the scoldings and makings-up of birds, the sharp crack of ice on a pond in winter, or the croak of frogs in the odorous evenings of June, and at all times of the year the welcome sound of a shrill voice calling me to supper. New England has something all its own — an atmosphere of rugged beauty, of kindliness hidden behind a brusque manner, that its people absorbed from the land; it is a country full of surprises and discoveries: lost ponds, unexpected vistas, hidden vales, villages cupped in unlooked-for hollows — unanticipated, breathless sights of the distant sea! I do not think

I was more sensitive to beauty than all the others, but perhaps I exclaimed about it more. It never failed me. And it never failed to excite and stimulate me.

Our Lancaster Township was a splendid kindergarten for an inquisitive boy. Within a day's travel I found and studied a great part of the geographical forms that mark the fascinating surface of the earth: it was not from books that I learned what a cape may be, a promontory, a tableland, a mountain, an inlet. Thoreau was beginning to translate Nature into our American language at that time; through his eyes New-Englanders saw beauties they had missed before. His exuberant joy over the mountains and intervales, the valleys and ponds, was communicated to me. I fell in love with my own country and its various and peculiar charm delighted my boy's heart and mind. I might add that the variousness of natural things in New England extended to the weather, but if I said that my New England friends would charge me with being a Californian now, and prejudiced.

As a child, my mother and sisters told me long afterwards, I was always a lover of flowers. I don't know whether it was the bright color or the perfume or the texture, or all three, because I certainly don't believe that I was a child-prodigy or a naturalist in my cradle, but certainly I have been told anecdotes enough of myself to show that I could be kept quiet and happy if I had a flower to hold and admire. This instinct or passion or preference continued after I grew old enough to choose my own activities, but I was a healthy, normal boy, I guess, and I can well

imagine that flowers appealed to me in inverse proportion to the amount of time I had to spend hoeing
them or fertilizing the ground or digging up bulbs in
the fall. I cannot remember that I was more interested in flowers or, indeed, in plant life than I was in
everything else about me. To the contrary, I am
sure that it was life that absorbed my attention. I
had no early tendency toward science, but I had a
consuming curiosity — an inquisitiveness — about
life forces and processes and miracles of Nature.

One incident, written clearly on the tablets of my
memory, concerns a winter-day discovery that gave
me a great deal to think about. I was heartily tired
of winter, I remember, as a growing boy in New England was likely to become, and was walking in the
timber piece, perhaps moodily, and maybe kicking
up the snow and calling it names, and perhaps
punished for my petulance by stubbing my rebel-
lious toe against a hard-hearted old New England
rock, when suddenly I saw a green place ahead of
me. I could not believe my eyes. There were tall
grass, bright, fresh, spring-like shrubs and vivid
vines, and on it all played sunshine that was almost
tropical in its white intensity.

I am sure I must have hurried forward, forgetting
my rebel mood, to find that this was all real — a sort
of winter oasis of green in a world of monotonous
white. It took me some time to make out that here
there rose one of those marvelous springs sometimes
found in wintry countries that brought to the surface
enough heat so that no snow could remain on it, and
so that vegetable life could get a foothold and maintain itself in the bitterest weather. I studied the

phenomenon intently. Very dimly there began to grow in my mind vague questions as to how these plants and grasses and vines, their neighbors and cousins and brothers all dead and withered under the snow, or else dormant and waiting for spring, could adjust themselves to this summer-in-winter environment. Why, I asked, didn't they follow the traditions of their families and die with the fall, or droop and shed their leaves and hibernate, no matter what the warm water brought to them in the way of a miracle of equable temperature? Certainly the lycopodiums, the beautiful trailing partridge berry, the sedges and grasses, and here and there an early sprouting buttercup, should have known better, the way they had been raised and with their decent seven-months-of-summer ancestry behind them, than to flaunt themselves so shamelessly in this unfilial winter blooming!

I am sure now that my first thoughts — very dim and vague, as I say, and only a boy's surface wonder, instead of a scientific hypothesis — concerning the power of environment in the miracles of plant variations came to me in that hour. It was late when I started home, and I could hardly wait to get there to tell the folks what I had found. To them it was no miracle; they saw in it no half-revealed secret stolen from Mother Nature's cupboard of marvels; but to me it was the most wonderful thing that had ever happened. It turned me to watching and studying and comparing, and when there fell on me the influence of an older mind trained in the processes of Nature, I was wide awake to make the most of the opportunity.

This older mind, that exerted itself strongly in shaping mine, was that of my father's nephew, Levi Sumner Burbank, a man who had been well educated, who had a bent for the natural sciences, and who certainly had a remarkable power of exposition and explanation so that what he talked about was alive and exciting and never dull and tedious. Cousin Levi had been a professor in Paducah College, and had read more books and understood them better than any one else I knew. My own father was well-read and my mother was versed in a knowledge of simple things, but Levi Burbank had matters at his fingers' ends and could talk of them fluently. He was interested in Nature and her processes and he knew enough of such laws and speculations as men had then formulated to open many doors for an avid boy. It was he, I think, who may have crystallized my formless thinking and shaped my vague theories until he had made me want to know, not second-hand, but first-hand, from Nature herself, what the rules of this exciting game of Life were.

These, I am sure, were the factors that led me to my career. My heredity gave me the basic plan for my building; the environment of that New England farm and the influence chiefly of my Cousin Levi showed me early something of the form the edifice was to take.

Afterwards I had the beginnings of education along many lines, but in my formative years I was moved only by enthusiasm, a love of Nature, a great and insatiable curiosity, and a high regard for facts as against theories. When I began to work I had no elaborate equipment — I had a garden patch; I had no microscope and Gray's botany — I had a hoe and a pair of overalls; I had no fixed and inflexible scientific education — I had a voracious appetite for knowledge. I have studied and experimented with plant life for almost seventy years since then; I have watched men and their motives and movements with interest and curiosity; I have regarded the progress of the world and what we call civilization; I have tried to look beyond war for its causes, beyond poverty for its economic germ, beyond ignorance for the sapping parasite from which it grows in the human mind, beyond bigotry and superstition for the human weakness and fear that breed them; I have wondered and questioned and experimented and observed, from the beginning until now, with no more equipment than the mind of one inquisitive and a lover of life, and now I look back down the years and try to set forth here something of what I have observed.

I had a taste for drawing and for a time I studied that art seriously; I had a good many inclinations toward the practice of medicine and I took up that training; there was every opportunity for me to go into manufacturing and I was given a place in a factory and for many months believed that I had, perhaps, found my work there. My employers felt this even more strongly than I did, particularly because, almost at once, I found short-cuts which enabled me to improve on their methods. Several of the devices which I invented were adopted and made a part of the factory equipment; I was told that I could advance myself rapidly with them, and my wages were, for that period, very high as a result of my adaptability and the inventive faculty I possessed. But, without my being fully aware of it, Nature was calling me to the land, and when there came to me my share of my father's modest estate I could no longer resist the call.

In Lunenburg Township, not far from Lancaster, I found seventeen acres of unusually fine soil that was for sale. On the place was a good old house and, although some of my friends tried to dissuade me, and the men at the factory told me I was making a mistake, I bought this property and set myself up as a market gardener. It was my notion that the garden would pay its own way and leave me not only a field for experiment, but the means with which to work; oddly enough it was not my instinctive desire to investigate the laws of the plant world, but a cold necessity which pitched me, as we say, 'neck and crop' into plant experimentation.

Immediately I began this vocation of mine I learned what all of us have to learn who enter the sober business of Life, namely, that I had not been the first to think of raising produce for the market. In short, I found myself in active competition with well-established and experienced market gardeners; of course I learned all the tricks of the trade as regards cold-frames, hot-beds, the use of water and fertilizer, and the cultivation of the soil, but my competitors all knew these secrets and used them better, probably, from years of experience, than could I, a mere youngster. This competition made me a serious student of the methods by which Nature produced variations in plants because I soon determined that success could come to me only through raising better vegetables and delivering them to the market earlier than any one else could do. Taxing my wits to find a way to make my garden pay, I came to my first constructive contact with the mysteries and miracles of Nature and that contact resulted in my life-work.

Better vegetables, I saw at once, meant, not only the best seeds and roots to be had, but the best that could be produced. In those days, with very few exceptions, no one had paid much attention to this ideal — this 'best that could be produced' — and what we had to take was what we could get. That set me thinking. To produce vegetables more cheaply than the other gardeners meant cutting corners in production and marketing, and there my Yankee instincts, I suppose, served me well. But what instantly fascinated me was the thought of producing vegetables of fine quality and getting them into the market ahead of every one else. Here was a goal for any inquisitive and active mind! Here was something you could get all excited about! Here was a place to use wits and ingenuity and inventive faculty and another faculty that, at the time, I did not know I had, even latently — the power of choice as between two apparently identical varieties or even between two apparently identical plants! Looking back I envy myself the thrilling and inspiring research and experiment that these considerations opened up to me, as though by magic!

My mind went back to the winter garden I had found in the woods, as a boy. There Nature had deviated from her apparent law of seasons and produced summer plants in the dead of January. How?

Obviously the deep-flowing spring, with its warmer waters sufficiently contrasted in temperature with the bitter cold of New England to temper the atmosphere where they rose, made growth possible, but I knew enough to know that vines and shrubs and flowers grew according to their season and withered according to an hereditary tendency that had impressed itself on them through thousands of generations of growth. The warm spring accounted for the equability of the temperature in that spot, but it did not account for the luxuriant and lush growth of plants that should be dead. What I had supposed was a fixed and immutable law of Nature was not, then, fixed and immutable at all. Or, better, the law was there, but I had misinterpreted it. What was the influence behind this phenomenon?

It was presently clear to me that hereditary traits and characteristics could be overcome, modified, changed, and adapted. That much, though perhaps not in so many words, I had for a starting-point. I began to experiment with plants, in a crude, superficial way, without any order to my trials and without keeping any record of results.

I found certain plants that grew more rapidly than others in the same row, and some with foliage better suited to the purpose of a market gardener; as, for instance, such as would give the fruits a better opportunity to mature, or such as would better shelter delicate ones, and so on. As the season advanced I marked individuals that bore more than their fellows; here and there I found those that bore bigger produce, or more succulent, or earlier or later. In each case I was looking for an improved variety —

improved in one respect or in two or three — and when I found a plant that was willing to take a step forward, I tagged it with a medal of honor and so marked it for further promotion.

When harvest time came these marked plants were saved and their seeds or fruits went into my 'stock' for the next year's planting. Stored in every cherished seed was all the heredity of the variety, and in addition a tiny spark of genius — of improvement — that environment (or, in some cases, perhaps, a mere chance) had placed there. In the beginning I had no assurance that the improvements would be absolute and fixed in the second generation, but after a time I began to see that they were, and that there was certain to be at least part of the second year's growth that would show all the finer characteristics of the marked plants, and a tendency to improve on their improvement.

It was not long before I knew that I was on the right track. My start had been made.

II

THE place where most stories of my work would begin, I suppose, is with my finding of the potato seed-ball that gave me the Burbank potato. That was an important discovery to me, and it did set my feet finally and successfully on my road. But I have thought often lately that if it had not been the potato it would have been something else, for I was determined before that time to find the vulnerable spot in Nature and make her my co-worker with plants; nothing could have delayed me long, and it was only fortunate, probably, that the incident of the potato came as it did, and so hurried things on for me somewhat.

The potato story has been told again and again, often correctly, and I am only going to summarize it here. In New England we grew large quantities of potatoes, but they were generally small, of a reddish color, and few of them good keepers. It required no genius to know that if a large, white, fine-grained potato could be produced, it would displace the other varieties and give its discoverer a great advantage over his competitors. I tried crossing with poor results, for the hybridized blossoms produced no seed. And selecting led me nowhere.

Then I found a potato seed-ball! I use an exclamation point. That is because — well, it was what an astronomer would use if he discovered a new solar system. A potato seed-ball was not unheard of, but it was a great rarity, and I couldn't learn of any one who had done anything about the event even when it occurred. I *did* something; I planted the seeds in that ball. I had twenty-three seeds and I got twenty-three seedlings. From that whole number, although there were many that were an improvement on any potato then grown, I selected two that were amazing, valuable, and a distinct type. They were as different from the old Early Rose as the beef cattle of to-day are different from the old Texas long-horn.

It was from the potatoes of those two plants, carefully raised, carefully dug, jealously guarded, and painstakingly planted the next year, that I built the Burbank potato. And it was from the Burbank potato that I made my beginning as a plant developer. Not only did the new potato prove to me that Nature was ready to coöperate and collaborate with man, but it made me a small name and paid me some small amount of cash. Both of these were important factors in my career. They are important factors in the career of any young man, and those who affect to despise either are talking rubbish. Money and fame, if you go out after them without any other motive, are a pretty low aim, but if your goal is service or expressing yourself or making the world a better place in which to live, you will find that a respected name and a few dollars in your pocket will grease the runners considerably! You'll go farther with less strain on the trace-chains and you won't tire so easily on the first short hill.

Meantime there were influences in my *environment* that I did not reckon with, and yet that determined my life for me. Let me give you a notion of how environment seems to me to operate and do its work on the living individual — plant, animal, or man.

It is not the duration of an environment that affects heredity; it is the amount of pressure exerted. The more sensitive the plant or the man, the more readily he takes the impressions his surroundings or situation give off. It is all a matter of vibrations — a matter of response to vibrations. In no other way than through vibrations do we get anything. You know that the camera plate is struck with blows of light to burn into the sensitized surface the picture you want to take. If you make what is called a time exposure the blows are gentle, but sooner or later they make a dent in the gelatine. The lighter parts are burned deeply, and the shadows and black places are only just touched. But it is the steady tap, tap, tap of the rays of light that do the work.

We are all made — plants and fish and cats and elephants and men — of organisms built of tissue that is built of cells. The life force is in the cells — protoplasm, made up of almost everything in the universe in infinitely minute particles. Now, because that protoplasm which, Huxley says, is the basis of life, is made up of almost everything in Nature, it responds to almost everything in Nature. Protoplasm is the sensitized film on our bodily and intellectual plates; vibrations from about us strike it and gradually they make a dent. Repetition, repetition, repetition — that is the process by which environment bends and moulds and directs and diverts and changes us. Why does the great composer choose two or three little phrases of music and work them into his symphony in a thousand different ways? Why does the orator use the same simple line again and again and again, playing with it, decorating it, embellishing it, speaking it in a low tone, then in an abrupt voice, then as a question? Why, simply to carry his message home! We say: Give a dog a bad name and you might better drown him! Because the badness of the dog is stressed day after day, month after month, until the whole neighborhood believes he is bad, and after a while the dog himself begins to figure that there may be something in the idea.

Perhaps one of the first words I ever heard was California. Certainly there must have been talk enough about this country, for the year before my birth was the year in which gold was discovered here, and in the ten or twelve years following emigration had set steadily this way from every part of the land. Moreover, my older brother, George, had come here in 1854 and his occasional letters (he was not a letter-writer, but a man who did things and left the talking about them to others) undoubtedly fired the interest of the older people and the curiosity of the boys. All that I heard of California day after day, week after week, from every side and source, even during a time and in a neighborhood where slavery and the strong will of the South were lively topics, impressed itself on my mind. I do not know that I ever suddenly announced my belief that California would be the place for a plant experimenter to work; repetition, repetition, repetition struck the storied name on my consciousness until I was as certain to go West as I was to continue plant experimentation.

This seems to me a happy moment to take one more step with you in the scientific course necessary to an understanding of much that I will write in these rambling papers on the work and memories of my years.

Remember that I was a New England boy, bred and born; my heredity might have been supposed to keep me a New-Englander, and my environment to double the urge. Instead I am writing of the certainty that I would pull up stakes and go to California. Was that chance, or an exception to the rule? Haven't I been saying that heredity gives us the foundation from which to build and environment shapes and designs the building? The explanation is simple; it relates so closely to all that is to come that I must give it to you here.

In the first place, you must look considerably below the surface to determine just what your heredity — any heredity— actually is. For into it, through the long line behind you, have come many and varied influences. And one of the most potent and revolutionary influences is that which results on the mingling of heredities through the mating of two sexes.

We accept sex as a fact and we accept the necessity for two sexes as a similar fact. But did it ever occur to you to wonder why Nature bothered to require two parents? I mean by that question to ask you to forget everything you know about the matter and consider it as though the whole plan of life were being instituted for the first time, and you were sitting in on the conference on ways and means. You would agree that there must be a law to compel

the individual plant or dogfish or toadstool or lynx
or ape or man to desire to live, otherwise the first
discouragement met with would be the end of that
enterprise! You would agree, secondly, that the individual must be compelled to want to reproduce
himself, or else the job of starting him off would have
to be done over and over again. So you would be
unanimously in favor of the law of self-preservation
and the secondary law of the perpetuation of species.
Very well; why not let each individual leave a cell
somewhere in a warm protected spot and then lie
down and die, assured that the nested cell would be
born into a copy of the original, and the species or
family would go right on?

I don't think it was accidental — this arrangement that required two cells to meet and join to reproduce themselves in a new life. Not at all. I think
it was for the very best reason that there is for anything in the miracle-working of Mother Nature. I
think it was because she knew that sameness, mo-
notony, exact reduplication over and over again
would make this world the dullest point of light in
the whole universe. Nature required variations,
change, development, growth. She may or may not
have wanted improvement — there is a great quarrel among the scientists on that fine point and I'll
pass it by for the moment. She did demand change
— variation — a constant blending of old stocks to
make new forms, shapes, sizes, colors, and to make
it possible for the individuals, whether plants or
animals or humans, to move about and adjust themselves to new conditions and so give the earth the
diversification and interest that it has for us to-day.

If the aster had re-created itself from one cell, it would have been an aster and no power on earth could have developed it into a coreopsis to the end of time; if the Burbanks had been blacksmiths, and none of the strains brought into the family by the women they married had exerted their hereditary influence, I should have been a blacksmith, and probably a poor one, and nothing could have changed me or given me a different chance.

Nature saw all that, and, by the simplest and most adroit single stroke that the whole history of biology records, made it impossible. She went a step farther and attached certain penalties to the single-cell or single-strain method of reproduction, so that what we call inbreeding is known to be a very risky thing to try, and cousins who marry often bring forth weak or sickly or defective children. No, Nature wanted variations, and she made it possible to have them from the very beginning — indeed, made it pretty difficult not to have them. And there is something you won't find in most of the textbooks, and I think you will find it something worth musing over!

This cunning provision Nature made brings us back to my discussion of the influence of the environing gossip and excitement concerning California on my New England heredity. That heredity had in it, not only the Burbank strain, but it had in it the pulls of my father's mother's heredity, and his grandmother's and hers, and so on, back and back, until I was related distantly, perhaps, to half the white people in the world; more than that, it had in it the pull exerted by the heredity of my own mother, a

Ross, and her people, on both sides, spreading later-
ally and running through the tree of the families of
earth until, on her side, I was probably related to
the other half of the world's white inhabitants. In
short, I was a product of all my heredity. And Mark
Twain was not altogether joking, maybe, when he
said that he had to abandon his efforts at getting up
a genealogical tree for himself when he discovered
that it included a horsethief or two. If there wasn't
a horsethief or an embezzling bank cashier somewhere back in my line, I am certainly different from
most folks; if you want to make a family tree that
will really tell the whole story, you will have to go
on below the ground (something I notice the gen-
ealogists are all too canny to do!) and follow the
roots from tap and anchor main stems through the
laterals and branches to the very tiny little threads
at the ends — and even then you would only be
starting your task!

I had, you can see, a variety of influences on me
that were purely hereditary. Who can say whence
came the strain that responded so instantly to the
repeated call of California? But it was there, and a
tug-of-war probably went on, without my knowing
it, between that strain and the hard-headed New
England blood of me. For New-Englanders are no-
toriously fixed and set sorts of folks; they are the
oldest Americans, they are well satisfied where they
are, they are conservative, they are not always chas-
ing will-o'-the-wisps. Even their famous seamen —
wanderers, pioneers, and adventurers though they
are and always have been — usually come home.
The New England heredity exerts a strong influence

on all its youth to strike their roots still more deeply into the parent soil. It was a battle between the conservative that said, 'Stay where you are!' and the radical that urged me to get out and go West.

For you must not suppose that heredity is only a matter of red hair or speaking German or bearing a family resemblance to your father and grandfather. Heredity is also a matter of ideas, ideals, habits of thought, points of view, temperament, and all the other mental and intellectual aspects of a man. The heredity of the Navajo Indian is not only toward a lean, long frame, an aquiline nose, and a natural ability as a hunter and a horseman, but it is toward being a wanderer; the heredity of the Hopi Indian is not only toward being shorter, squattier, heavier, slower, and broad-nosed, but it is toward being a town-dweller and a trader, with a timid sort of agriculture on the side.

You see, we are a bundle of hereditary strains and tendencies; environment may play on one or two and not on the others, or it may act strongly on half a dozen or all of your inborn characteristics. In my case some untraced tendency was toward movement away from the home-place: my sensitized plate was struck repeatedly by influences leading toward California. I had no choice in the matter. I was bound to go!

Now we come to another very important influence that operates on our hereditary tendencies to change and modify and direct them into new channels — the influence of education. Education is a form of environment — an intellectual environment that is as definitely moulding and directing as the pressure of a rock on a plant to force it to creep toward the light, or of a spring of water to give it the strength to grow taller than its kind.

I am not speaking of my education by books in the schools. I am a good deal of a crank about the education of children, and probably I won't be able to contain myself on that subject as we go on; right now I have in mind the influence on me of the greatest scientific thinker of our age — the man who changed the whole meaning and language of science, Charles Darwin. In Lancaster I had got hold of a book of his: 'The Variation of Animals and Plants under Domestication'; it opened a new world to me. It told me, in plain simple sentences, as matter-of-fact as though its marvelous and startling truths were commonplaces, that variations came from cross-breeding, and that these variations seemed to be susceptible, through selection, of permanent fixture in the individual. While I had been struggling along with my experiments, blundering on half-truths and truths, the great master had been reasoning out causes and effects for me and setting them down in orderly fashion, easy to understand, and having an immediate bearing on my work! I doubt if it is possible to make any one realize what this book meant to me.

Big as the book was, and significant as it was to me, its influence over me was heightened and its lure for me was increased by the uproar with which its author's theories were received. In 1859 Darwin had published 'The Origin of Species,' and just when 'The Variations of Plants and Animals under Domestication' was stirring me all up, he shook the

world with his 'Descent of Man.' Almost immediately the storm broke, especially in the New England churches and homes. The theory that man had
descended from an ancestry common to that of the
apes — Darwin never said anything about his *de-
scending from monkeys* — was blasphemous, scur-
rilous, infamous, and other things even worse! Darwin was banned from the churches and from most
homes, and those who read him were considered as
bad as he was. Perhaps I was always 'ferninst the
government' as they say; at any rate, the man every
one was discussing and most of them were damning
was for that very reason interesting to me, and the
controversy — a rather one-sided one in our neighborhood, I remember, since there were few to defend
him — only served to inflame my interest in every
word he wrote. The blows his personality and
phrases struck on my sensitive mind were steady,
sharp, and persistent; my New England heredity was
outweighed by the pressure of my environment —
the talk of California, the furor against Darwin, and
his clear and illuminating book — and I pushed out
and away.

I check myself here to be sure that I am telling
the whole story, and a little guilty feeling comes
over me. The fact is that there was an immediate
cause for the ultimate act of severing home ties and
setting out for the West. I am sure now, and I think
I was sure a few months after my arrival in California, that I was certainly destined to make the break,
but if I had been asked as I boarded my train for
the great adventure just why I was going so far
away, with such apparent suddenness, I should

have replied sadly that it was on account of an un-
requited love.

The story of this early romance of mine has crept
into the newspapers now and again; the truth is that
I was very deeply fond of a beautiful young lady who
seemed to me, I remember, less ardent than I was.
A trifling disagreement, two positive natures, probably hasty words — and I determined that my
heart was broken. To be frank, I think I gave that
affair to many as my reason for coming West.

Mary and I can look back now on those tragic
days — for I am sure they were tragic to both of us
— with smiles; shortly after my arrival from California I wrote her, or she wrote me, and we resumed
our friendship by letter. The friendship has been
kept up all these years and has been very significant
to both of us; probably my Mary of those old times
has had many an occasion to be thankful that I took
her at her word when she told me — as I think she
must have — that I was not the only eligible young
man in Massachusetts! There is the story, in a few
words, of the early romance that drove me West.
It was the proximate cause, probably — the turning-point. And it was rather heroic and romantic to
use as an excuse for this dramatic move in my life.

I find, on looking back through letters written
home at the time, and on considering all the facts
that there was another motive behind my decision,
although I am not at all sure that I was conscious
of it at the time. There are in those first California
letters several references to the sense of freedom
California gave me, and now I can say that I was
undoubtedly influenced by a desire to be my own

man, unadvised by family or friends, and no longer compelled to explain or apologize for my choice of work or the methods I employed in getting at it.

There are, I have observed, many proverbial adages that tell only a half-truth, if that much; one of them is the saying that a rolling stone gathers no moss. It may be a fact that the young man who doesn't know his own mind about a life-work and who is always jumping from one thing to another will never get anywhere on the straight, long road, but I am not so sure that this isn't due to maladjustment to his environment rather than to his instability. On the other hand, the stone that is planted in the home field and never stirs from there is pretty certain to gather nothing but moss and so to become that other proverbial monstrosity, a moss-back! My belief is that you will find most of the men in the world who have accomplished something have done a considerable amount of rolling in their time, and have gathered a large amount of the varieties of moss that are most useful to us all — experience, adjustability, adaptability, facility, acquaintance, breadth of view and vision, and the chance to learn just what it is in the work of the world that is most useful for us to do. I do not insist that all young men and women should up stakes and move, or that those who do so are bound and certain to succeed just because of that. But I do maintain that the law of change, variation, new environments, and new developments of the individual as a result is a definite law of life. I am a poor hand at forcing advice on any one, and particularly on the young, but I will say that, if your present surroundings or environment or situation seems to you to hamper and restrain and hobble you, a sharp break with all that is old and settled and habitual to you may save you from becoming a cog or a barnacle.

It was in 1875 that the stories of the West, Darwin, my unconscious sense of restraint in New England — and Mary — sent me packing. I was twenty-six years old — a small, wiry, active young man, observant, alert, inquisitive, and full of ideas about what I was going to do. A few very definite fundamental laws of Nature were fixed in my mind as a basis on which to build. I had read more science than most youths of my acquaintance, and all that I had read had been illuminated and crystallized for me by Darwin. In my luggage I had ten Burbank potatoes that I had been permitted to retain when I had sold the new variety to a New England seedsman. They were to be the foundation of my fortune and the beginning of my fame. I meant to round out both fortune and fame. It was some years later before I reached a turn in my road where I had to decide between them and my work: that is an interesting chapter in these papers that must come in its turn. For the moment I was pretty definitely fixed in my ambition, and the bigger, broader, more important meaning of life hadn't come to me. I expect that the first person singular of the personal pronoun was the one I employed most in my thoughts, whether I used it in conversation or not.

That one-letter word 'I'! For some years now I have been more proud than of any other one thing in my career that I have deleted at least a million 'I's' from my own manuscripts or from those prepared about me by others. Here they keep cropping up like the blotches in measles! They tell me that, in such papers as these, they cannot be avoided. I shrink a little from each one of them. I have been so long accustomed to fighting them off. But perhaps one can get used to them. Whitman used them more than any other man, perhaps, who ever lived; he said he was preaching himself to the world because he did not think he was far different in his nature and reactions from the general run of men. And, turning to an old and well-loved volume, I find Henry David Thoreau boldly stating his same case in these words, in his book called 'Walden':

I should not obtrude my affairs so much on the notice of my readers if very particular inquiries had not been made by my townsmen concerning my mode of life. . . . In most books the first person is omitted; in this it will be retained; that, in respect to egotism, is the main difference. We commonly do not remember that it is, after all, always the first person that is speaking. I should not talk so much about myself if there were anybody else whom I knew as well. Unfortunately, I am confined to this theme by the narrowness of my experience. Moreover, I, on my side, require of every writer, first or last, a simple account of his own life, and not merely what he has heard of other men's lives; some such account as he would send to his kindred from a distant land; for if he has lived sincerely it must have been in a distant land to me.

That is good. I will write of this Harvest of the Years of mine to you, my kindred, as though from a distant land!

III

THERE was a time when, looking back over my early years, I was inclined to glory in the fact that I had made a success for myself and of myself when I had started humbly and without much money or a college education or what we call a silver spoon in my mouth. I classed myself, I expect, with other Americans whose names are known and connected in every schoolboy's mind with poverty bravely endured, hardships undergone, and mean tasks well performed; in short, I was rather fond of the American log-cabin-to-President tradition.

Now I wonder if this whole business isn't rather empty! I don't believe I ever had a moment's pity for myself because I was having a hard row to hoe as a young man making a start in California. The fact is that America is great, not because her poor boys have struggled through difficulties and become successful, but because there are here great difficulties to be overcome. The struggle has brought out the best inherited tendencies and potentialities in her men and women when their environments have been poor or simple or their chances meager. It is this environment that is changed by the American environment of education, ambition, opportunity, and the rivalry to excel; these factors or forces operate, when the heredity is sound, to give us our Presidents and our captains of industry, our thinkers and writers and artists and scientists and leaders in every line.

No one ever heard Abraham Lincoln tell the now-famous story of his having learned to cipher by scrawling sums on the back of a wooden shovel with a charred stick, lying before the fire on his stomach, and the picture we have all seen that shows him at this elementary education of his is one I will bet a shinplaster he did not pose for! Andrew Carnegie was a telegraph messenger; Rockefeller started as a clerk with a produce commission house and was paid fifty dollars for his first three months' work; John Wanamaker began as an errand boy and Thomas A. Edison as a train-newsboy; Theodore Roosevelt was born of well-to-do people, but his early years were the hardest of all because he wasn't well and had bad eyesight. But what of all this? Most of our big, busy men, who have done something with their hands and brains and time, have known what it was to have a toe stick out through an old boot or to have to face company because of a social discrepancy in their trousers' seats; and when I think it over I am suddenly minded to say that they were all the better for it and might not have got much of anywhere if it hadn't been for the very tests and trials to which Life put them!

There are a bale of stories about my own early hardships — some of them I scarcely recognize and others I have heard so often (and perhaps told; who knows?) that I believe them myself; yet when I examine them now, thinking over the harvest of my years, I can only say: 'Well, if those things actually happened to me, as some of them undoubtedly did, I learned through them and took courage from them and got experience out of them and was made better and stronger and more self-reliant by them, and they were milestones on my road and not millstones around my poor, bowed neck at all!'

I am through with the log-cabin-to-President tradition for good and all; hereafter the only man I am going to be sorry for in our land of opportunity is the man born with a silver spoon in his mouth!

A very moving tale could be woven out of my first years in California, but an old letter which I wrote back East a few days after my arrival, shows me that I had about everything that would make life interesting and worth living to a young man with great ideas of what he was going to do with himself. The first sentence I encounter, in looking at that epistle of my youth, recalls one of the favorite stories of the log-cabin-to-President writers who have fooled away words on my biography: the anecdote has been embellished and worked over until you might believe that I began my Santa Rosa experience in a chicken coop because I couldn't afford better quarters. Well, here are the facts:

Brother Alfred and another fellow have put up an 8 × 10 shanty and I expect to go to keeping house with them to-morrow. We bought crockery, bed-ticking, etc., last night. . . . I shall not look for work for a week. The change of climate has given me a cold, as it does nearly all, but I never felt so *contented* and free from mental disquiet, and never slept or ate better in my life.

A fog is hardly ever seen here — the wind never blows hard. I wish you could see California fruit. I bought a pear at S. Frisco when I thought I was *hungry* for 5¢. It was so large that I could only eat ⅔ of it. I threw the rest away. Grapes are so abundant that all are allowed to help themselves to the nicest kinds at the vineyards.

There is no skin to them and very small seeds. The pulp is the whole grape. If you try to squeeze one out it will split like a plum. They are very sweet and nice and are so plenty that they are often used as hog feed.

The italics were those of my youth: also the hand-made abbreviation for San Francisco.

You can't feel sorry for that boy! In fact, I envy him! I would give a good deal right to-day to swap places with him; to go out to-morrow and buy crockery and bed-ticking, etc., for the 'shanty' and to start housekeeping with Alfred and his friend (whose name I have long since forgotten; he was only with us a few weeks). That shanty is still standing in Santa Rosa, and is now used as a shed or chicken coop. That is how that story got going; it is too bad to correct so beautiful and inspiring an error, but you must make the best of it. I didn't begin life in California sharing my roof with the chickens, and it is quite apparent that I was well-fed and happy when a bunch of grapes could send me into rhapsodies and '⅔' of a five-cent pear could satiate me!

Another letter, written at about the same time, has some valuable material in it; it shows how I was impressed by my new environment, and it also shows that I early developed a caution in public utterances that stood me in good stead many times later. This letter is marked 'Not Public,' and it reads, in part, as follows:

The reason that I give this description of Santa Rosa outside my general letter is because if it is generally known what a place this is all the scuffs would come out here, get drunk and curse the whole country, so don't let on to *anybody* outside the house what sort of a place this is *except* that I am delighted with it.

I firmly believe from what I have seen that it is the *chosen* spot of *all this earth* as far as *nature* is concerned, and the people are far better than the average. The air is so sweet it is a pleasure to drink it in. The sunshine is pure and soft, the mountains which gird the valley are very lovely. The valley is covered with majestic oaks placed as no human hand could arrange them for beauty. I cannot describe it. I almost have to cry for joy when I look upon the lovely valley from the hillsides. The gardens are filled with tropical plants, palms, figs, oranges, vines, etc. Great *rose trees* climb over the houses loaded with every color of blossoms. Do you suppose I am not pleased to see the fuchsias in the ground 12 ft. high, the trunk 10 inches in circumference, and loaded with color? . . .

A *family* can live here, I am quite sure, for about one-half what they can there and far more comfortably. Meat costs but little, flour is better and cheaper, fruit is nothing almost, very little fire is needed, and such warm, expensive houses are not necessary. . . . Have given you a truthful description of my experience so far.

I came across a directory of this country just now. I take a few ideas from it. The cause of the great growth and prosperity of this place (Santa Rosa) just now is the new railroad which has given it a start. It is the county seat and is called the prettiest town in the state. It is noted for its polite and obliging people. . . . It is situated in a marvelously fertile valley containing 100 square *miles*. The educational advantages are ahead of any Cal. city of its size. (The above is from the directory.)

Wasn't that parenthesis astute?

But I was always on the trail of my life-work, or the other way round! In a letter written November 9, 1875, I encounter this paragraph:

I took a long walk to-day. I found enough new and curious plants in a wild spot of about an acre to set a botanist mad. There is an old surveyor who knows nearly all the plants here. I am going to take a batch to him this evening. He is very much interested in them. My botany tells the names of only a few Cal. plants. Some of them *have no names*.

Later on in the same letter I read: 'Have a job of lathing for next week.' As a matter of fact, I failed to get it, but that mattered little.

Charles Darwin's 'Cross- and Self-Fertilization in the Vegetable Kingdom' was published in 1877 and it was not long before I had a copy. I had spent my first months in California studying the country, comparing various localities as to suitability for my purposes, earning my way with whatever came along to be done and experimenting with plant development. I soon knew most of the native plants and herbs that came under my notice and I remember being greatly interested in the California poppy, which I had never seen equaled for color and profuseness of blossom — the hills being mantled with them in the late spring until it was easy to believe early discoverers might have given the opening to San Francisco Bay the euphonious title 'The Golden Gate' because of the color on the Berkeley hills opposite that entrance to the harbor. Later I had a lot of fun with the poppy: by carefully planned cross-fertilization and then selection I was able to get color in the poppy from the clearest white to a deep red. At any rate, from the first I found plenty to interest me and plenty to study before I came upon Darwin's new book.

One sentence in the very introductory chapter of that volume opened the door of my mind and took possession of my fancy. After discussing briefly the marvel of cross- and self-fertilization in plants Darwin said:

As plants are adapted by such diversified and effective means for cross-fertilization, it might have been inferred from this fact alone that they derived some great advantage from the process; and it is the object of the present work to show the nature and importance of the benefits thus derived.

Advantages and benefits! Darwin was writing of the plants themselves — I was thinking of mankind. If Nature had developed an incredible system by which plants could re-create and diversify and improve themselves *for their own benefit* and advantage, why should not Nature be induced to employ that same system *for the benefit and advantage of man?* It was my starting-point — and it was Darwin again!

You see, we have a lot of new wants coming on all the while — it is the natural thing with man. The first main want is food, then clothing and shelter. If we can get plants — not just a few plants, but all plants — to produce food, we have certainly accomplished something that is the most important of all, perhaps. Then another thing — flavor and keeping qualities — all these things are wants. Flavor is just as important as nutritive value, because people generally cannot digest things as well if they have not a pleasant flavor. Food cooked by an artist will keep a man in absolutely perfect health, while food cooked by a bungler will drive a man to drink as sure as fate. I've been accused of exaggerating the importance of this, but I don't mind. I declare that a meal prepared by a person who loves you will do you more good than any average cooking, and on the other side of it a person who dislikes you is bound to get that dislike into your food, without intending to.

Then we need shelter. We need trees that grow very rapidly — more rapidly than those we have now. We need those that produce lumber — durable lumber, and lumber for different uses, whether for building houses or making axe helves. There are various uses for very strong and very fine lumber, increasing all the time. We need fuel, of course, although that need is being met by development of electricity by water power and coal.

Then we need clothing. We need hemp and flaxes and various new plants that will produce more fiber for less labor and that will do this on less land without taking any more from the land. This last is a point often overlooked, yet of the greatest importance. In America we feel we have all the land we need — that we have land to spare. But if you are looking for a farm, for instance, you will find this is hardly true. Millions of acres of land are not tillable or have no water. The good land is pretty well all in use. Some of it has been practically used up and must be made over either by Nature or with artificial means before it can be used again. The best land costs so much that you can hardly afford to pay the owner a premium for giving you a whack at it. And so we are, to-day, right up against the problem of making the land do more work with less exhaustion.

We need, moreover, a great many other things that we do not now produce in America, but that we could produce. Take rubber as an example. There is a great hue-and-cry because it costs as much to put new tires on an automobile as it used to buy a good team and side-bar buggy! We are dependent on other countries for our rubber, and there is no reason why we should be. I notice some of my friends in the rubber business have wakened up to the possibilities here; — I talked to one of them about it a few years ago when he was here and he pricked up his ears and looked as though he had caught an idea or so! We can do anything in America we set our minds and hands to doing; if we have one weakness more dangerous than another, it is the weakness of being satisfied and complacent about things — of not getting stirred up enough over our own lacks.

There is another need we have; the need for more beauty. We have neglected this aspect of life too much; we have taken what we had and not minded very much to increase our æsthetic appetites or to feed them. We need beautiful lumber and we need shapely and beautiful ornamental trees; we want fragrant flowers — a thousand things that make life well worth living in the shape of ornament and beauty and things that, to many of us, seem superfluous, or at least not absolutely necessary. But they are, just the same!

These are only a few of the possibilities in plant breeding and development. They were possibilities when I started in, and they are still possibilities. I could see a great many of them, and I began to try to work some of them out. It is interesting to me in retrospect, to recall that I was, in most senses, a pioneer in this chosen field of mine, and I think this fact stimulated and urged me on. There were no precedents to go on in plant development. Darwin had experimented with pollinization, but only for the purpose of discovering and setting down laws. He made important and absolutely new findings, but when he had made them and set them down he left it to others to make the rules useful.

There had been plant breeding in England, where they had worked with roses, and in Holland, where there had been great interest in tulips. I think, too, that there had always been a more or less unconscious selection practiced, maybe all over the world. For instance, the ancients who planted figs or pomegranates undoubtedly took their cuttings from the best and biggest trees that bore well, and so they developed generally some good figs and pomegranates — by selection, without their calling it that. There hadn't been, though, any broad experimentation or research or practice of this business of improving plants so that they would be of more use and benefit and advantage to man.

Right away I found that all the facts in life and Nature are correlated; I saw that this specialty of mine, that you might think didn't amount to much and that any first-rate gardener could contrive, was a sort of cross-country trip through the whole field of natural science. To arrive anywhere you needed something more than a definite idea of your destination — you needed a diagram of the lay of the land all around.

But that is true generally; it is something all of us, no matter what our job in life may be, might be better off for considering. Because you cannot judge *a man*, for instance, by studying him alone, or even by studying *man* alone; you cannot know much about an elephant by studying elephants alone; you have to learn about habits and tendencies and surroundings and about the things on which the individual is dependent and which go to make him and his actions possible or necessary, as the case may be. You cannot become an authority on grasses — the grasses fit to eat and those not fit to eat (all grasses fit to eat have seeds) — just from studying grasses. No, the fact is that you cannot see all of the facts about anything by just looking at that thing itself. To learn part of the essential truth about grasses, for instance, you have to study the cow!

When you delve into one little narrow subject, such as plant breeding, we'll say, or the barber trade, or keeping house, or operating a telephone switchboard, the more you know about chemistry and astronomy and human nature — nature in general — the more successful you are going to be. Because you know where to place each fact that comes to you in your training and your practice. You see, if you do not know where to place your facts they are not good for much. A fact is relative, and if it is placed out of its relative position it apparently is not a fact, often.

But get your facts to line up in their proper position and everything is all right — like soldiers. A general gets them lined up and he can march them forward to accomplish whatever he desires; so unless facts are marshaled together — substantiate and complement each other — they are not worth much. Some people bear down on a single fact and wear it all out, but there are other facts related to that fact which, if they were brought together and put in their proper order and sequence, would illuminate a whole city street. That is what I discovered very early in my work — to get at all the facts on every side of the subject, and then when I went ahead I knew my way and wasn't groping around or barking up wrong trees or wasting time building fine theories on unstable premises.

At that time I had a pretty good background of scientific reading. I had had ten years of actual work with plants and a life-time of interest in them and curiosity about them, and I had fundamental rules for my work pretty clearly in mind. But how could one man, in his single lifetime, have much of an influence on the vegetable world, when about all that most experimenters in any line had been able to do was to specialize on one single branch and die leaving the work unfinished? Here I was, keen to break trail in every direction — to improve ornamental trees, to find some laws about lumber trees, to make more beautiful and finer and more gracious flowers, and to give the farmer and gardeners of the world earlier varieties, better flavored fruits and vegetables, sturdier and heavier-bearing grains, and more profitable varieties of all sorts and kinds. It was a large order!

IV

I HAVE noticed that many things come to the man that needs them and needs them for a really important reason. Not Fate or Kismet, not divine intervention or providence; we get ourselves all ready for the critical moment and adapt ourselves to the favoring environmental influence eagerly and instantly — as quick as a shark will grab some lazy fish! And so it sometimes seems to be almost prearranged for us. At about the time I was beginning to develop my work in a broad, comprehensive, sweeping fashion, an incident occurred that crystallized everything for me.

A man wanted twenty thousand prune trees delivered within nine months, because he was in a hurry to plant his orchard; no one could accept the order because there were few nurseries in those early days and the ones there were didn't have the stock. I was approached. I didn't know how it could be done, but my brief experience in working with Nature instead of following set rules made me feel there ought to be some way. I had neither twenty thousand prune trees nor any place from which to get them. But I began to reason it out. I have made it a rule all my life, by the by, never to sign papers or obligate myself to anything of importance without letting the proposition lie around in my mind for twenty-four hours; on this prune-tree proposition I needed the time and took it; the next morning I accepted the order.

Now I was not only given a chance to try out some of my theories about this collaboration with Nature of which I have spoken, but I was squarely up against the necessity for doing it. For some time I had realized that there were two entirely new channels through which to move in training plants to work for man, and this prune order made it necessary for me to put both of them into employment. First, I felt sure that I could bring about, in a few plant generations, what Nature required hundreds or even thousands of years to achieve; secondly, I saw that such experiments as I would have to conduct must be performed, not with one or half a dozen plants, but on a broad scale — literally by wholesale. In short, to borrow the language of industry, I not only had to *speed up production*, but I had to *build up and maintain quantity production!*

Nature, as I have already shown, appeared to me to demand or require or call forth variations and the adaptation of those varieties to new environments. But she had all the time there was and all the raw materials she needed; she could be wasteful and extravagant, on the one hand, and leisurely, on the other. She worked with birds and bees and other insects in cross-pollinization; she was assisted by all sorts of accidental hybridizations; she sowed seeds far and wide, employing floods and winds and glaciers and migratory birds and animals — these were only a few of the agencies used. She made millions of trials and had millions of failures, but she had no reason to be concerned about that. She wasn't under contract, and no one was writing her indignant letters beginning, 'In the matter of the shipment of pine trees ordered from you five hundred years ago for our temperate climate beg to advise you that same has not yet arrived.' No, Nature employed the system of trial and error, trial and error, and yet eventually there was dispersed over the whole earth the multitude and infinity of plants and shrubs, vegetables, and flowers, fruits, and vines both that we find in the wild state to-day and that, working with the wild plants as foundations, man now has to fill his gardens with delight, his orchards with plenty, and his fields with wealth.

I could learn my methods from Nature, but I was not compelled to accept her schedule. I was convinced that, by following her system and learning lessons from her open book, man, with his developed intelligence and his lately acquired habit of aiming at a definite goal, could get, in plant breeding, what he wanted, where he wanted it, and eventually about when he wanted it. The prune-tree order was necessarily a wholesale job, where I could try myself out in handling large numbers, but primarily it was a test of my ability to accelerate Nature's methods by intelligent employment of her laws.

The first requisite for the new venture was a sturdy but rapidly sprouting tree stock, and I chose the almond because, unlike nearly all stone fruits, it takes hold readily and grows quickly. I found twenty thousand almond nuts of even quality, spread them on a bed of coarse sand, covered them with burlap, and on top of the burlap put a layer of sand. The purpose of this arrangement was to enable us to examine the sprouting nuts daily without disturbing the roots; in fourteen days a few of the seeds had sprouted and were picked out and put in the nursery beds; as fast as sprouting occurred the planting followed, and by the last of June those almond seedlings were up high enough to be budded.

Meantime I had arranged with a neighbor to furnish me with twenty thousand prune buds, and early in July and all through that month and part of August I had a large force of experts budding the prune buds into the almond seedlings. After about ten days I found the buds would make good unions with the stalks; then, in order to force all the nourishment into them, I had to find a way to eliminate the almond side of the family without killing the young trees. If I had cut the almond twigs and leaves off summarily the seedlings would have died; instead I broke off the tops and left them hanging — there was still a connection, but most of the strength of the little tree was diverted to its adopted child, the prune bud.

The plan worked perfectly. The prune buds took hold bravely and in a few weeks what had started out as an almond was a prune, and flourishing mightily. By December 1st, 19,500 prune trees were ready for the order, and the delighted customer said I was a wizard and paid the bill with great satisfaction. That satisfaction, I do not need to add, was mutual, because I had not only proved my theory that Nature could be hurried and used and directed by man, and in wholesale lots, but I had silver jingling in my pockets and the necessary capital to go on with the great work this first effort now opened wide to me.

Ever since that time I have worked on a quantity

basis, speeded up. This does not mean that I ever overlooked quality; on the contrary, it was only to get quality, and a very definite sort of quality at that, that I was working at all. I have had as many as ten thousand separate and distinct experiments going on at one time. I have produced as many as five hundred varieties of plums on twelve trees in one short row. I have had in my gardens as many as eight thousand different varieties of roses, iris, or gladiolus. Every one of these was obtained by using natural processes or adaptations of them, and every one was there because I needed it in my search for a definite quality or characteristic. I took Nature's mind and added to it my own, that knew exactly what it wanted and was in a hurry (comparatively speaking) to get it!

How did I operate in carrying on these experiments?

This is not a manual of hybridization and selection; I fancy you would find that pretty dull reading. But the general underlying principles of the work may be mentioned, and they seem doubly important to me because they concern all life and, if they are rightly read, will throw light on a lot of the puzzling facts of our existence and of the existence of conditions which we find about us and with which we have to contend in the struggle and loss and gain of our lives.

I have referred to the importance of combining our heredities so that we get variations — powers and characteristics and capabilities and possibilities that could not come to us from one straight and undeviating line of ancestry. Compare the Chinese

and the native-born American, and you will see
what 'mixing up' the strains can do. The Chinese
have, to be sure, absorbed several alien bloods in the
centuries past, but pure Chinese has been the dom-
inating influence on all the people. The result is that
they are conservative, not adaptable, with cautious
minds and reactionary tendencies, worshiping their
ancestors and the past and not looking forward nor
trying to improve themselves or their own conditions. Occidental influence (environmental) is beginning to stir them up some, but the hereditary pull
is too strong. Nothing will radically alter the
Chinese race but crossing with some other strains.

The American, on the other hand, is related to
most every white race on this planet: we have
English tenacity, French enthusiasm, Celtic im-
pulsiveness, German inventiveness, Scandinavian
loyalty — some of the best and a few of the worst
tendencies of a mixed heredity. The result is that we
will tackle anything and, while we may brag and blow
a little too much, we usually come out with what we
went in after.

That is crossing; — that is, in a sense, hybridization. The tiny cells in which the life force is stored
meet and are united. If there is the same heredity
behind each, the mating is smooth and uneventful.
But introduce a strange or alien heredity and there
is an explosion such as you would get from touching
off ten thousand tons of dynamite in a concrete
warehouse! The atoms fly in every direction; everything is broken up at once and millions of tiny constituent particles are blown entirely out of the
record! Some few unite, and from them come the

new individuals, having something of both heredities and yet new characteristics and characters and tendencies and potentialities not to be accounted for by anything we can put our fingers on in the past lines.

I often think that I had something to do with dignifying the word 'hybrid' — I hope I did. Because hybrids are what make the world go forward. They give us our inventors and poets, our dreamers and leaders of the earth, and in the plant world they are the fragrant and gracious flowers, the luscious and nourishing fruits, the succulent and meaty vegetables. Have you ever noticed that the most intelligent, the most loyal, and the most friendly dog is usually a mongrel — a cross between two good strains, with a little sense of humor interjected from some early indiscretion on the mother's part with a dog who was not all he should have been?

This is not to say that all mongrels turn out well — most of the litter in which your smart dog was whelped will be hardly worth drowning! But the combination of heredities often eventuate in an individual pup or cat or mule or man or flower or fruit that will stand out away beyond any of his fellows, or of his parents, because from all the possible hereditary influences in all the lines behind him the best have happened to be caught in his particular bundle. That super-intelligent and valuable mongrel dog of yours is a hybrid — the explosion caused by the meeting of the alien cells has resulted in good characteristics from all the respectable families behind him and a little saving grace of original sin from the gardener's dog!

In my work with plants I deliberately crossed

different individuals and varieties. This is an operation that looks simple, but whether you get results or not depends on your gift and practice and hand and eye. I like the old story about the great artist who was asked with what he mixed his paints to get such marvelous results, and who answered, 'I mix them with brains, madam!' He didn't mean brains, precisely; he meant his own gift for color and for its application to the canvas. Pollenization can be learned by any one, but only a few have the instinct that gets results. That is no credit to them — it is just given them, like red hair or Edison's genius for chemistry and physics or a good cook's pie-crust. This hybridization was done in Nature's gardens by the insects, the birds, the winds, and so on; in the plant experimenter's grounds it is done by hand. Nothing left to chance or occasion, but all planned and timed and regulated. There is the first step in plant development.

The second step is selection.

Nature selected by a law of the survival of the fittest; that is, inherent fitness — the fitness of the plant to stand up under a new or changed environment. It was the plant's business and had little or nothing to do with what man would consider, from his standpoint, the *improvement* of the plant. There is a kind of grass that grows on the Pacific Coast that shoots up tall and straight in protected spots, which is its natural home. Seeds were carried out along the seashore, though, where the wind blows hard and constantly. The grass had to accommodate itself to this new environment; many of the plants died — thousands — maybe hundreds of

thousands. But those that bent themselves to the
wind and survived put a new quality or tendency
into their seed; in generations the pull of heredity to
make the grass tall and straight had been overcome
to such an extent that the grass was dwarfed and
almost crept along the ground. The environment
had changed the nature of the plant, and now we
find two kinds of grass, of precisely the same original
strain, yet so different now as to be almost unrecog-
nizable as the same variety. Plant a seed from the
tall brother along the shore and it will almost
certainly be killed by the wind. Plant one of the
dwarfs in a protected spot and it will continue to
grow dwarfed for some generations, if it survives.
It might not live, though, because the soil that had
once been its home, or the particular temperature or
moisture conditions that favored its brother, might
not be suitable for it in its new character.

That is selection by the law of the survival of the
fit to survive. The victor in this struggle — this
competition for life — might or might not be a plant
more beautiful or more useful to man; it would only
be the plant which had succeeded in adapting itself
for its own benefit. I availed myself of this natural
process — this law — in making my selections, only
instead of selecting by means of deadly environmental competition I selected with a knife, or a hoe,
or a spade and a bonfire.

Hugo de Vries, the great Dutch botanist, was very
much interested in this wholesale method of mine
and in a book which he wrote on his theory of Mutation he commented on it in these words:

One very illustrative example of Luther Burbank's methods must suffice to convey an idea of the work necessary to produce a new race of superlative excellency. Forty thousand blackberry and raspberry hybrids were produced and grown until the fruit matured. Then from the whole lot a single variety was chosen as the best. It is now known under the name of 'Paradox.' All others were uprooted with their crop of ripening berries, heaped up into a pile twelve feet wide, fourteen feet high, and twenty-two feet long, and burned. Nothing remains of that expensive and lengthy experiment, except the one parent-plant of the new variety.

The second step — selection — is taken at different stages in the development of the plant, depending on what I am seeking to attain. There is nothing like this sort of selection, as practiced by the plant developer, in any other line of work I can call to mind. Breeders of fine animals, horses and cows and swine and sheep, and so on, come the nearest to it. But they are looking for one or two qualities, whereas I must look for many — and must stay with it until I get them. The horseman wants strength or speed or a high-headed horse or a show horse or a gaited horse; the cattle breeder may want a big milker or a big cream producer or a big beef strain, and that is about all he can expect to achieve.

But I start by wanting good form, size, spread of leaves or branches, and general appearance and sturdiness in all my plants, whether an amaryllis or a walnut tree; after that I may want a heavy bearer or a bearer of a few large blossoms, I may want fragrance, or may want color, I may want a thin-skinned fruit, or a fine cooking fruit, or a good shipper or keeper. I have almost limitless needs in

my work, and some plants have to be taught or
trained or bred to give me one simple new characteristic and others to give me a dozen. So you can
see that I have to select and re-select again.

We must not overlook, here, another sort of selection that goes on before and after the selection as
between two or two thousand individual plants or
trees for the sake of getting a desired variety. This
perpetual selection — this watchfulness and caution and care in seeing and acting on the difference
between grades or qualities — begins in many cases
with the seed, when one must sift the chaff from the
wheat, the even, well-developed kernels from the
irregular or faulty, those that are too small or too
large, those that are scarred or bruised, and so on.
In some cases, again, the germinating sprouts show
differences, and those that would be a waste of time
or garden space must come out. The plant develops, and again the weaklings or the awkward ones
or the misformed ones must be eliminated. So it
goes on — selecting, selecting, selecting, first to see
that your raw materials are the best possible, and
then, when the time comes, to choose as between individuals with an eye single to the purpose with
which the whole experiment was begun.

It is when the time arrives for this selection for
qualities sought in the plant or tree that almost any
one would like my job. For then a thousand shades
and variations appear, a flower gives perfume that
never had it before, another shows a variegated
color scheme, another has drooping petals for
straight, or straight for drooping, or a vegetable
astoundingly exhibits a new quality or flavor or

some amazing trait never seen before by mortal eye. These unexpected variations I speak of are in addition to the ones for which I am looking and on which, especially in later years, I was able to plan fairly definitely. And if I am working with a fruit, and usually with the vegetables, too, I may not start selecting at all till the fruit or vegetable is ripe. In that case there is quite a lot of fun and interest, not only for me but for the whole family, because we go right into the kitchen or to the dining-table with our products, and we preserve or cook or make jelly or soup or stew, and selection becomes a matter for palate and nose, or even for the stomach and the digestive processes, as well as one of eye and touch and æsthetic measurement.

It was in this instinct for selection that I was gifted. It was born in me, and I educated it and gave it experience, and have always kept myself attuned to it. I have particularly sensitive nerves — that accounts partly for my unusual success in selecting as between two apparently identical plants or flowers or trees or fruits. There is certain music I cannot listen to without pain — and I am not making a joke there! What I mean is that some notes and vibrations in music hurt me physically, and I have once or twice been forced to leave a room or a hall where music was being played or sung — and beautifully, too! — because the strains hurt me. I have always been sensitive to odors, so that I could detect them, pleasant or disagreeable, when they were so slight that no one about me was conscious of them. My sense of touch is almost as acute as that of Helen Keller, who visited me just a short time ago and with whom I could converse easily — more easily than most — because we were so nearly equally sensitive.

Probably there is more to it than merely this sensory response in me — it may be a sixth sense, it may be purely intuitive — but I know that even those who have worked with me longest and have been closest to me, learning my methods and watching me in the gardens, have been unable to duplicate what I have done as a mere matter of routine, and with no thought as to how I did it. Some of the men who have worked for me have developed into good, sound, original, and even clever and successful, plant developers. But as far as I have been able to observe they have not been able even to approach my own natural ability to choose between plants, and to choose, not one from a dozen, or a few here and there, but at wholesale — thousands of plants in a day out of tens of thousands growing in my experimental gardens.

Even close friends and observers have said what you, perhaps, are saying to yourself now; that is, that I was bound to be right part of the time and that there is no way of telling how many poor selections I made through error nor how many perfect ones I caused to be destroyed. My friends were wrong, as you are. I make some mistakes, of course, but considering the number of plants I have selected in the course of sixty years as a plant breeder they are negligible. On the contrary, I will tell you a story, out of many such that are available, to show you how complete my gift is.

From the first it has been my practice to mark selected individual plants by tying a strip of old white cloth on; this means that that marked plant is sacred, and you would soon notice that the men working for me would give one of the 'neckties,' as we call them, a wide berth. Plants that I could see would add nothing to my experiment, by any possibility, came up at once, or else were marked by my making a line in the bed with the toe of my shoe so that the men could take them out later. This left, of the hundreds or thousands of plants concerned, a large number that were tolerated, not so much because they had individual merit — though they sometimes developed that, here and there — as because watching their progress might throw some light on the experiment. Now, when I had a very large project going on — a field or bed with thousands and thousands of varieties or individuals in it — I would have two or three of my helpers follow me and I would simply drop the 'neckties' on the superior plants or those suited to my purpose, and put a shoe-mark against the worthless ones, about as rapidly as a man could walk along, and the men would do the tying and spade out and burn the condemned plants.

I was engaged in selecting from some thirty-five thousand plum seedlings one day when my friend, the late Judge S. F. Leib, of San José, drove in. I went on with my work, but I saw that he was concerned about the growing pile of young trees being heaped up to be burned, and sure enough it wasn't long before he stopped me.

'Burbank,' he said, 'I have the utmost confidence in you and I would believe anything you told me

about your work, but I can't think that you are
right in uprooting all those beautiful seedlings and
sending them off to be destroyed. It looks like a
shameful waste to me.'

'Well, Judge,' I said, 'this selecting isn't being
done by guesswork, though I suppose it looks like it.
Why don't you take half a dozen of those condemned
trees and plant them down on your Santa Clara
Valley place, and find out for yourself whether I am
right or wrong?'

He said he would like to make the test, and for
good measure I insisted on his taking also six of the
seedlings I had selected as the best varieties. So we
dug the trees up carefully, packed them, and shipped
them to his home. I saw him once or twice a year,
at least, and sometimes oftener, and the test of the
trees was mentioned occasionally, but it wasn't until
the fifth year, when the trees had had a chance to
develop and come into bearing, that he made his re-
port.

'Burbank,' he said then, 'if any one had told me
five years ago that selection could be done by a man
almost at a trot, I would have said that he was crazy.
I have been an orchardist for years and I think I
know something about horticulture and plant development, but what you have shown me beats anything I have ever heard of!'

Then he went on to admit that he had been wrong
and that I had been right in every single case. He
said that he had ordered his men to take out and
burn all of the six trees I had condemned as seedlings,
five years before, but that every one of the six I had
chosen had proved perfect trees with beautiful luscious, well-developed fruit and plenty of it. He was

very fond of telling that story on himself, and he did a great deal, as he had done before that incident, to help me with my work and to give me confidence in myself and give other people confidence in me.

If you will stop a minute to consider you will see that I had to be accurate in selecting, or I would have wasted half my time growing varieties and individuals that were useless to my experiments, or else I would have done what Judge Leib thought I was doing — thrown away or destroyed thousands of plants with possibilities. No; the fact is that I have a gift for selection that I suppose very few men in the world have ever possessed in any line. It was a straight benefaction to me from my heredity, somewhere away back, and environment — my work and my need for a selective faculty — developed it, and education — experience and watchfulness and study — perfected and polished it. But to it I owe a large measure of my success, because it made possible the conducting of an enormous list of separate experiments, most of them done on a very broad scale; without it I could not have worked with so many kinds of plants nor done so many different things with so many different varieties and species.

Hard work, application, study, love of the task, the desire to cover a wide range, and the ability to learn from Nature and then to select accurately as between individuals of apparently identical character — these have been the basis of my achievement — these are the foundation stones of success in plant development and improvement, and it was these that have made it possible for me to give the world so many new creations in flowers and grains, fruits and vegetables, shrubs and trees and vines.

V

THERE are no statistics at hand, but I suppose I have had as many visitors as any man of my time anywhere, and have made as few visits as any. Of those who have come many have been customers, many scientists, many famous men and women; the great bulk of them, though, have been just plain people interested in flowers or trees and in what I was doing, and who were ready to go out of their way to visit headquarters.

The stream began to flow early, but it did not reach any considerable proportions, except as regards customers who came, from the beginning, to buy potatoes or nursery stock, until I made an announcement, which I will come to presently, that caused folks everywhere to prick up their ears. How they came then — and how many of them there were who expected me to be a sort of museum curiosity, and my gardens a side-show! I can remember well how their attitudes changed when they saw what I was doing and that I was only a man, after all, with no signs of hoofs or horns, and wearing everyday clothes instead of a masquerade-ball costume! From that day to this my callers have been interested, thoughtful, mannerly, and kindly, almost without exception: I have had in my home and on the farms thousands, from street-car conductors to the King of Belgium, from laborers to Mr. Edison, from housekeepers to Paderewski, from primary-school teachers to Helen Keller, and pretty nearly every one of them respected my work and my ideals and my knowledge of my trade, and showed that they did.

In the seventies and early eighties, when I first began to sell nursery stock in Santa Rosa, there was a great demand for such wares, and I realized that this business would give me room and equipment for experimentation along my chosen line and at the same time would pay expenses. I started with one acre of land; by 1883 I had eight acres, in two plots, and was looked on locally as one of the successful nurserymen of California. Emerson is credited by some with saying that the world will beat a pathway to the door of any man who makes a good mouse-trap; the fact that I sold only the best nursery stock and stood behind it with my own personal guarantee brought me plenty of customers.

By comparison this policy of mine, too, was welcomed at that time. It was a period when the whole country was overrun with traveling agents. Lightning rods, sewing machines, cookstoves, household doctor books, farm machinery, crayon enlargements — pretty nearly everything a gullible countryman might get himself all tangled up with was sold from door to door, from farm to farm, by glib salesmen with spanking 'turnouts' and a beautifully illustrated catalogue that made a person's mouth water just to look at the cover. Nursery stock was sold in the same way; it is all recalled to me by encountering, in an old scrapbook, a piece I wrote for a paper in which I said:

After several years' preaching on how to make trees live, I cannot be contented until I have given you the improved method for killing them.

The first and most important step is to buy half-dead, sickly, scaly, refuse trees of some honest traveling agent, who in sweet and mellow tones will tell you he is the only person who has a stock of the kind you are looking for.

I found customers for that kind of sarcasm right away; the next issue of the paper contained a communication from a man in Nevada City, California, who wrote that he had been defrauded by 'an agent from around the Bay who traveled with a big album under his arm, full of the most gaudy, highly colored illustrations of fruits and flowers — which the same, by the way, is the kind of molasses used to catch country flies.' I had hit the right spot, but the traveling agent flourished for a long time and did a great deal, not only to cheat and swindle people who were setting out orchards, but to delay the development of the State by broadcasting inferior nursery stock.

I stressed the fact, from the first, that I hired no agents, and as time went on the street in front of my place was crowded with teams, especially on Saturdays, when the orchardists from as far north as Mendocino County and as far south as the Santa Clara Valley would line up to buy Burbank trees. But the mere business of selling was irksome to me; I have never liked commercial life nor dealing with men on a basis of barter. Some have supposed this was because I was not a good business man, but instead it is because I early acquired the scientific point of view which does not take money or what the world calls success into account.

This is not a pose with scientists: your merchant or banker deals in and handles money — it is the measure of his business and the medium of his mental activity; the scientist deals with truth, and the more of it he can accumulate in his life, and the better he invests it in research and experimentation, the greater his success. A business man is not accused of putting on airs when he says he wants to make money and has no time for art or science; no more should a painter or a scientist be accused of posing when he says that money means nothing to him. The first is dealing with money and money-making; the latter is dealing with beauty and basic fact, and he would rather get along with very little in order to have his mind free from obligations to deliver at so much an hour! Some folks see this, but it is a truth all may well ponder, because it seems to me to express pretty clearly the difference that exists between commercial men and men of creative bents or scientific achievement, without at all belittling either.

I sold nursery stock, you might say, as a side line; for by this time I was in a position to put into practice the theories I had as to the great importance of experimenting with plants in the search for varieties more useful and beautiful and productive than those we then had, and I was beginning to get my stride in quantity production. This preoccupation of mine escaped most of my immediate neighbors, who knew me as 'the Santa Rosa nurseryman with the place south of the iron bridge'; away from home, though, I was beginning to be known, especially by men interested in plant breeding and, to a limited extent, by the professors who expound science, and the scientists who promulgate its laws.

My original marketing of the Burbank potato won me no recognition from science, because it was merely the more or less fortuitous development of a new variety. You see, it was something as though a prospector had discovered a new gold field; the geologists and mineralogists would know all about gold and the mere addition of a new field wouldn't concern them much. But when I began to establish the fact that I could train old varieties in the plant world to new habits and possibilities and could produce entirely new varieties with characteristics and values never known before, I was more like a man who has taken known metals and from them extracted radium. The moment I emerged as a scientific experimenter and investigator the scientists wanted to know more about me.

Very slowly, but surely, the word spread that there was a young fellow out in California who made claims about plant breeding that had never been made by any living human being on this planet before — and not only that, but that he was showing his wares as proof. I began to get letters and inquiries about my work, and after a while I had a large number of contacts, faint or strong, indirect or immediate, with the world to which I was to belong from that time on — the world of science.

There were some other contacts being made at this time that proved in the long run to be of the utmost importance to me and to my work. They began with an idea I had that California seeds might be interesting and useful to foreign seedsmen; there were large and old firms scattered about Europe and England and down in Australia, and I wrote some of them offering seeds, and particularly California wild-flower seeds.

Much more quickly than might have been expected I built up a good business in this line; very few people know it, but the fact is that California wild-flowers and native plants have been transformed or developed into some of the favorite garden plants of England and the Continent. That I contributed something to this result is perfectly plain.

The work gave me much satisfaction and pleasure and some cash. It brought me into touch with the whole world of men interested in flowers and plants, not for the sake of their anatomy or leaf-structure or Latin names, but for the sake of their beauty and utility, and it was an inspiration to me to find everywhere men of high standing and well considered in their own lands working away at something like my own job. I remember that it was a delight to me to get away from my farms on Sundays and wander about the hills and along the coast gathering seeds. Of course, as in the work in my gardens, I had to visit the plants first when they were in blossom and select the ones I wanted, marking them scrupulously so that I could find the plants later.

I always used strips of cloth or bits of string as markers, and often I would find myself out of cloth so that I would be compelled to tear up a handkerchief or perhaps borrow the end off a Christmas necktie in order that some precious plant might not be lost track of. On more than one occasion I was reduced to using a shoestring, and several times I labored home along a dusty road with my shoes flapping up and down at the heel like a Chinaman's slipper. But when I went back at seed-time, I would always find my selected plants (if a cow or a deer hadn't found them first!) and then I felt repaid for my efforts and my mother and sister would be reconciled to the disappearance of my haberdashery. For it was unusual for me to make one of these trips without bringing back, in addition to seeds for my export business, some new and perhaps, to me, priceless trophy — a seed-pod, or a bulb, or a pollen-laden blossom, to use in my own experiments.

One of the earliest connections made in pursuit of the foreign business was with the firm of C. Platz and Son, at Erfurt, Germany; I have a letter from them, dated 9th January, 1886, in which they wrote, in quaint English:

We have much regret to hear from you so long time nothing. Therefore we profit from the occasion to beg you to will address to us one of your special offers of the seeds native in your country and of such which we have had before from you.

It would be very agreeable to us if our relations were renewed in a very lively manner, and you can be assured that we do all for to make the same so advantageous as possible.

Awaiting your kindly news we have meanwhile the honor to be, dear sir, Yours very truly . . .

I am sure I hastened to renew my relations with this kindly firm in a very lively manner; in fact my relations generally, throughout my life, were made and renewed and carried on in the liveliest manner of which I was capable, and what later became known in the business world as 'pep' and 'zip' and 'punch' were part of my make-up. I have never found that anything comes to the man who sits back in a chair, whether it be hickory, deal, or mahogany, and waits for something to turn up; the man who goes ahead is the man who does his work and sells his product 'in a very lively manner,' and he is also pretty certain to go a long way and to have liveliness become such a part of his mental and physical equipment that he can turn hand-springs at seventy without going to bed afterward with lumbago!

It was when I had this California wild-seed business going, and partly as a result of that business and partly as the result of my work, my announcements and the newspaper accounts, few and far between, of the line I was pursuing, that I began to make a series of connections referred to above that had so vital an importance to what I have done with plants. These connections were formed voluntarily by the other parties: from scattered points I began to receive letters from people enclosing seeds of strange, or wild, or unusual, or foreign plants, all of them sent with the hope that they might be of interest or of use to me.

I cannot tell you how impressive these contributions were to me then, nor, looking back, how large they bulk in my mind to-day. In the beginning they were timidly sent, usually by reticent people who were not sure how their proffers would be received and who, I could tell from their letters, would not have been surprised if what they had enclosed were tossed aside or never heard from again. I do not believe any of them fully realized what amazing kindness they were doing me: not only did they contribute most useful additions to my materials for work, not only did they give me hints and suggestions of the greatest value, and not only did they show me how close my work was to the hearts of many people, but they brought me into touch with a whole world of interesting, romantic, colorful facts and localities and personalities, and with the flora of the entire world! There is no more beautiful chapter in the whole book of my relations with my fellow men than that which would tell the story of my happy relations with plant collectors all over the planet.

I want to give you just a taste of the sort of interest there came to me in these letters, and the sort of contributions made, by including here a few of the letters. In respect of their subject-matter all were different, but as regards the generosity of the senders, their common feeling about my work, and their unselfish desire to help me and to contribute to the task I had set myself, they were very much alike, from the beginning.

From the whole mass (I have a trunkful of them!) I select one first that came many years ago from Papua, in New Guinea, and I do not need to call your attention to the dramatic nature of the simple story contained. The letter reads:

DEAR MR. BURBANK:
Your most welcome and kindly letter found me 45 miles inland at Jawara Rubber Plantation, and came to help fan back to life the dying embers of my life!
On the road out the second night I was camped just under a grass roof. After getting to sleep, perspiring under a mosquito net, a N.W. squall came on and rain. I got a thorough chill. Next morning it was too wet to go

on. In the afternoon I set out and went a few miles to another plantation and camped there. Next morning set off. They told me the road was very bad. First we had to go through mud and wade creeks every now and then, then we had good going until we struck another creek, which we had to cross and recross and then follow up a good way. Then on the divide between these waters about one thousand-foot rise and after some distance, we dropped right down to another creek, about seven hundred feet in half a mile; then following this creek down for about seven miles in a deep gorge, crossing, recrossing and wading.

Well, I got to my destination. The valley is barely one-half mile wide and mountains three thousand feet high all round. I never was in a place with less air. In two days I got down with a sort of rheumatic fever and was laid up for over two weeks. It was a close go. If I could have had a hot bath it would have been all right, but I could get nothing except drugs which I never touch. One God-send, I had limes but not properly ripe. Mr. Griffin from Sogiri lent me some mandarin oranges which helped me a lot and your letter finished my cure.

I immediately proceeded in search of the seeds I have written you about. It is another rock melon which is used to the wet; the rainfall here is sometimes 140 inches. I also got seeds of cantaloupe that grows about six or seven inches in length and 3½ in diameter (wild). The natives grow them a lot. Considering the amount of wet they stand you ought to get valuable new blood. They are very nice as they are.

The man I was with tells me of a strawberry growing about four thousand feet up the range. He has the name of being such a liar that I don't know the truth of it. But there is a large plum, very acid. When you take the skin off it is almost transparent. I think this is a fact and therefore if I can get two mountain village boys to carry me over all the water I will go up and see if I can get some of these for you.

Trusting the seeds I sent after all this journey will be acceptable, with every good wish from

Yours faithfully

J. A. HAMILTON

Such service as that would be rare in a highly paid and expert collector financed by me; this man was a volunteer who did not expect money or even thanks for his services. As a matter of fact I always sent these unknown friends seeds or bulbs and, when they had been to expense, tried to reimburse them as fully as I could; even then some of them refused my money, and went on working for me — for my work and my purpose, I am sure, more than for me, personally! — for months or years or, in some instances, throughout their lives. Such incidents as these are among the precious and great things of life; they make one pretty short-tempered with the miserable, pestilential ink-fish who seem to reach their most bloated maturity in our modern literature, dyeing and staining it with the murky sentiment that it is vulgar to have a kind heart and middle-class to do beautiful and inspiring and helpful things for others or for the world.

Now here is another letter, from another kind of traveler, a gentleman of importance in the business world, who gave me just this brief insight into his interest, and suggested to me a whole bookful of adventure and exploration in one sentence:

I am hopeful that this corn will be of interest to you. When I went to visit the grave of old Cetewayo, the great Zulu king, I had you in mind. Zululand was the last place of interest I visited in my tramp across the Dark Continent from Cairo to Capetown.

There was a man who carried the thought of my work as far with him as he carried back the seeds which he sent me. Then there comes a letter from a woman who was interested and had imagination enough to see possibilities in what most would have passed over completely, and would have failed to relate to anything that is living or important to us and our children. It ran:

Under separate cover I am mailing you seeds which were taken from the cliff-dweller ruins in the Grand Canyon by an exploring party in 1893. When the seeds were given to me at that time, I placed them in a glass vial where they have remained ever since. There are five pumpkin or squash seeds, six or seven reddish brown beans and about two dozen kernels of corn. Not being a farmer, I cannot determine the vitality of the seeds. I notice that the kernels of corn are somewhat triangular in shape as though they grew on a well-packed ear.

I have a piece of the corn-cob which came out of the funeral urn that contained the seeds. If the old, dried cob has any resurrection value, you may have it also.

If you will think a minute you will see that there were two ways in which to use those squash seeds (that is what they were, I found — a sort of gourd) and the beans: they could have been analyzed and examined under a microscope and reduced to their component elements, and a treatise written about them that might have contributed a good deal to our knowledge; or they could have been put to the test of Nature. It was the latter course I pursued, because it was in that aspect of the seeds that my interest lay. Botany — the science of the physical structure of plants and their classification — is the study of growing things as they are or have been; my

work has been to see *what they might become*. Both
the scientific botanist and myself are working to one
end, along different lines; science — true science —
is closely related to human needs and wants and desires and our human pursuit of happiness, and that
is why it seems to me so wonderful a calling and ob-
jective.   I can't be very much excited about being
referred to as 'Doctor,' but I can be tremendously
excited about giving the world a better radish or a
zinnia with a new quality and color.

Well, I got away off the main track that time!

I find another letter from one of my volunteer
helpers: a picturesque young man who added interest to his contribution by sending his picture and a
view of the isolated part of the country from which
he was writing:

I am sending you under separate cover two beans
found in the cliff-dwellings on the head of the Gila River
in the Black Range Mountains of New Mexico. A bunch
of cowpunchers and I were working cattle in this country
and we decided to look the cliff-dwellings over. It is a
beautiful place seen only by cowboys.

We found five beans and a few grains of corn. We divided up and I got a bean and a grain of corn. I lost the
corn, worse luck, but turned my bean over to a mountain
farmer on the halvers. He planted the bean and I got five
beans for my part.

I have thought I would try my luck farming and raise
beans from these ancient seed for marketing, but I
thought you might do a better job, with your experience
with seeds, and try these on the shares.

If you should like any information about this I would
be pleased to hear from you at any time. I am enclosing
two photos taken on the trip, one of the canyon where the
beans were found and one of myself on the horse.

I wish you would notice that this cowboy got only five beans from his mountain farmer friend 'on the halvers,' yet that of those five he sent me two. Two fifths of a man's total capital in this line is something I can get worked up over — it is just plain unselfishness and the kind of confidence in you that warms your heart! I would have planted those two beans if I had suspected them of being pigweed.

I received invaluable assistance from many scientific men too; one of them was Mr. Huron H. Smith, of the Milwaukee Museum, who sent me, among other cherished seeds and bulbs, some contributions from an old Wisconsin Indian whom he called Uncle John. Uncle John never wrote me, as nearly as I can remember, but Mr. Smith was kind enough to forward some of the old brave's letters received by him, and from one of them I quote:

As partly being on a Daupt [in doubt?] on Mr. Jim's Tiny Potatoes for seed already sent you, have found stronger and larger ones to take place of Jim's. Send you to-day from Robert Pa-ma-po-my my neighbor who live close by me here some & will grow on new land to be quite large and long in length, in shape like powder horn or like new moon when first appears . . . You can do just to please with those 6 potatoes sent you. Probably replace [forward?] to Luther Burbank. Yes, probably there could be an Improvement made on the growing of other potatoes with those of the Indian potatoes sent to experiment with & if they do combine each together or some way to Bear then there will be then 'Half Breed Potatoes.' Oh how would they taste; well Bully?

JOHN V. SATERLEE

The volunteers helping my work now number thousands, scattered about the world, many of them in remote places. Those in Australia, New Zealand, Canada, and other English provinces and dominions were most numerous, perhaps because the English love gardens and understand them and because these people, some of them far from their native island, were caught by the nature and interest of the task I had set myself. I hope some day to be able to write more extensively about these helpers of mine, their adventures and discoveries, their perils and treks, their hopes and disappointments as volunteer collectors; certainly an interesting volume would be made — several volumes — from the letters to me from these friends I never met!

VI

My nursery business had gone ahead satisfactorily throughout the early eighties, but I began to discover that I could not carry the load of business and details it entailed, nor give the time necessary to seeing customers and talking to people about orders, with all that meant. I loved my work and I loved people. There was never a time when a man was merely a customer to me — unless it was when he failed to pay his bill and then I usually just cut him off the roll! So it was often a long job to sell a short order, because people wanted to visit and — maybe I did, too.

You can't mix visiting and hard, exacting work, though. In a way the man with a big job has to cut himself off from interruptions of all kinds. This seems particularly true to me now, when newspapers and magazines have made people accustomed to knowing about every one and every thing, so that they don't feel it is out of the way to ask questions and poke around. I don't blame them: I never could see a man operating a steam shovel or a structural iron-worker swinging on a girder high above the sidewalk or a woman running a new-fangled electric ironing-machine, without stopping to watch and wanting to ask something about the how and why of their jobs. But to the man on the girder questions might be a little out of place, especially if there was a good strong wind blowing!

I found I had to fish or cut bait, as the saying is,

and I decided to cut the bait. If I supplied the varieties and worked out the problems there were plenty of people handy at selling: presently I disposed of half of the nursery business and later got out of it entirely. I went at my work in the experimental grounds, and by 1893 I had a bombshell to explode.

It took the form of a catalogue, under date of June, 1893, and its title was 'New Creations in Fruits and Flowers.' Inside the cover page I made the following announcement:

The fruits and flowers mentioned in this list, and to be mentioned in succeeding lists, are more than new in the ordinary sense in which the word is generally used; they are new creations, lately produced by scientific combinations of Nature's forces, guided by long, carefully conducted, and very expensive biological study. Let not those who read suppose that they were born without labor; they are not foundlings, but are exemplifications of the knowledge that the life forces of plants may be combined and guided to produce results not imagined by horticulturists who have given the matter little thought.

Limitations once supposed to be real have proved to be only apparent barriers; and, as in any of the dark problems of Nature, the mental light of many ardent, persevering, faithful workers will make the old paths clear, and boundless new ones will appear by which the life forces are guided into endless useful and beautiful forms.

We are now standing just at the gateway of scientific horticulture, only having taken a few steps in the measureless fields which will stretch out as we advance into the golden sunshine of a more complete knowledge of the forces which are to unfold all the graceful forms of garden beauty, and wealth of fruit and flowers, for the comfort and happiness of Earth's teeming millions.

Nowadays, when we are accustomed to picking up the daily paper and reading that some heroic

LUTHER BURBANK AND A JAPANESE STUDENT HELPER IN HIS GREENHOUSE
AT SANTA ROSA AT HARVEST TIME

Note the variety of seeds gathered here. Mr. Burbank and Hasegawa are selecting
Burbank corn for the next year's planting

flyer has just crossed over the North Pole, or that a biologist we never heard of has found a new vitamin, or that a machine has been invented that will transform the business of keeping food iced in our homes, we might not be more than passingly interested in the announcement that a horticulturist had created a new kind of pear that would put all the known pears into the shade; in 1893 things were not moving quite so fast and a claim like mine made quite a loud noise in the sedate and mannerly period when the White House was occupied by President Cleveland and when Queen Victoria still had several years left of her long reign.

Prior to this I had sold several new varieties to the public or through big nurserymen, but here was a wholesale bulletin, proposing to dispose of almost a hundred absolutely new plants, flowers, berries, and trees together with complete rights and control, in each case, so that the buyer could be sure that he would have no competition. The list began with the hybrid walnut, which I called the 'Paradox' because it was a paradox that a hardwood lumber tree could be produced to grow as fast as the most rapid-growing and short-lived variety. The catalogue said of this tree:

The first and one of the most interesting of the hybrids produced among walnuts. Budded trees six years of age are fully twice as large, broad, and tall as Black Walnuts at ten or Persian Walnuts at twenty years of age. The leaves, which are from two feet to a full yard in length, are clean-cut, glossy, bright green, and have a surpassing sweet odor resembling that of fragrant apples and as powerful and peculiar as that of roses and lilies.

They scarcely believed that one — but they went away convinced if they ever saw it!

There were four new quinces, ten new plums and prunes, a large list of berries, a number of flowers, including the first double gladiolus ever known, with flowers closely arranged around the spike like a hyacinth, and my 'Silver Lining' Poppy, which, instead of being crimson and black on the inside is a glistening silvery white, the outside retaining the same brilliant crimson as its forbears. Finally the booklet was completed with an offering of vegetables of new variety and productivity. Near the end of the book, too, I find there was a picture of the blossoms of the cross with which I was then experimenting between the apricot and the plum — the first public reference, I guess, that was ever made to my plumcot.

In a statement at the end of the book I set down my whole theory of plant development, summing up all my knowledge and experience in a few sentences, and laying down the law in these words:

There is no possible room for doubt that every form of plant life existing on this earth is now being and has always been modified, more or less, by its surroundings, and often rapidly and permanently changed, never to return to the old form.

When man takes advantage of these facts, and changes all the conditions, giving abundance of room for expansion and growth, extra cultivation and a superabundance of the various chemical elements in the most assimilable form, with generous light and heat, great changes sooner or later occur according to the susceptibility of the subject; and when added to all these combined governing forces we employ the other potent forces of combination and selection of the best combinations, the power to improve our useful and ornamental plants is limitless.

It might be a good thing for you to have in your minds, along about here somewhere, that there is a great controversy among scientific people concerning the answer to this question:

'Do our changing racial and individual traits, observable throughout the whole realm of life, both past and present, come to us by inheritance — are the seeds all contained in the minute organisms from which life springs, or, on the contrary, do we acquire new characteristics, from our situation or necessities — our environment — and pass those new tendencies or abilities or powers on to our children?'

The question is whether all changes, which we notice in successive ages of life development, are traceable to heredity alone or whether we can 'inherit acquired characteristics.' The man who believes the former says that the loyalty, fidelity, and good nature of a fine police dog were contained somewhere, perhaps only potentially and not at all developed, in the wolf from which that police dog finally sprang. The man who believes that acquired characteristics can be and are inherited maintains, instead, that a pair of savage wolves can be caught and somewhat tamed; that their puppies can be raised in domestication and made a trifle less savage and treacherous: that after generations and generations the characteristics of gentleness and good nature and fidelity to a master become so impressed on the succeeding generations that there emerges finally a police dog which is only distantly like the original wolf parents, having *acquired* so many new characteristics and passed them on, bit by bit, in the blood stream, that the police dog is practically a new species of animal.

There is a great deal more to this controversy than my bare outline suggests even, but perhaps this statement is enough to explain the fundamental proposition disputed and to make clear what I am going to say in connection with my claim that I had produced 'New Creations in Fruits and Flowers.'

I myself have proved, beyond question or doubt, that new characteristics, foreign to anything in the heredity of the plants involved, can be and are so impressed in succeeding generations by my process of repetition, repetition, repetition, over and over and over again, and always for the same effect and in the same direction, that there comes out in the end through selection a new and distinct plant result. It was this conviction, in the face of the controversy that I refer to, that is expressed in the first paragraph of the summary I have given above. I stated that 'plant life is now being and always has been modified more or less by its surroundings (environment) and often rapidly and permanently changed, never to return to the old form.' This was strong medicine for the straight heredity theorists, and Balm of Gilead to those who believed with me. I am going on in a moment to tell you something of the processes I employed. In the meantime the catalogue had another far-reaching effect that was sensational and unheard of before. This was the amazement and indignation with which many orthodox people received the claim of a man to 'new creations.'

I could see, and did see, that the term would be

examined critically, but it had not occurred to me that it would be considered blasphemous. Not that it would have caused me to use other words if I had foreseen the storm; I have never been one to consider how my utterances would be received by others, so long as I felt convinced that what I said was sound, scientific, and accurate. I didn't think much about the matter from this viewpoint, to tell the truth, because I was so absorbed in the importance of my work and the necessity for impressing horticulturists with the significance of what I had accomplished. I spoke up and said my say, and then I went back to my job.

It presently seemed possible that I was going to have a good deal of difficulty staying there. A perfect storm arose, in the heat and wind of which I was called a good many names stronger than blasphemer; I was preached about, talked at, written, telegraphed, scolded, abused, and even vilified: the more extreme of my critics said that I was setting myself up as a competitor of Omnipotence, and the mildest of them called me a falsifier. One preacher inveigled me into his church, had me seated in a front pew, and then worked up a trap for me by which I had to say just what I believed as to the truth of natural laws behind all life and what I disbelieved as to the truth of metaphysical and superstitious theories concerning creation. When he had me, as he thought, in a fine bag, with the drawstrings pulled, he proceeded to berate me in good old orthodox style and ended by offering a prayer for my awakening. Of course I had neither thought nor said anything either impious or blasphemous, unless it is impious and blasphemous to work with Nature, utilize her laws, direct her work, apply intelligence to plastic forms, and then claim a victory in getting useful and beautiful results. But it was lively while it lasted!

Still another class of people were stirred up over that catalogue of mine, and those were the nursery-men and horticulturists. A good many of them had already heard of me or had seen some of my new varieties, and they were ready to believe almost anything I would seriously claim for my work. A good many had enough information so that they thought I might have accomplished a part of what I asserted for myself — they discounted me a little for exaggeration. But hundreds of them were straight-out skeptical, or even scoffing. I had said in the catalogue that I could not engage in long explanations by mail: they could either buy outright on the strength of my name and reputation or they could come and see for themselves. The result was that a shoal of them came.

I have always been fond of the story one of them told me afterward. He said:

'Burbank, I have traveled more than three thousand miles to see your grounds, and to find out about your assertions regarding your new fruit trees. When I got off the train this morning I happened to meet an old gentleman who said he had worked for you for years. So I asked him what he knew about you. He said:

'"Luther Burbank? Why, I know all about him! He used to have a big nursery, and he did well at it. But he sold out, and now he raises acres and acres of

all sorts of stuff and waters it and tends it and culti-
vates it through the spring, then when summer
comes he hires most of it plucked out and burned.
Burned! D'ye ever hear tell of such foolishness?
He's got a lot of trash left, and talks about selling it,
but I wouldn't give him fifty dollars for the whole
kit and boodle. That's Burbank!'''

This Eastern nurseryman laughed as he told me
the story. I went around the place with him and
showed him what I had, and he listened with more
and more interest as we passed up and down the
rows, and before he left he selected seven plants out
of my whole list of new creations, and paid me, cash,
six thousand dollars for them. He was satisfied with
his bargain, too, and made money out of it — big
money, he has told me since — and from that day to
this he and his sons, who followed him in his business, have been among my best customers and
strongest adherents.

Well, the nurserymen came and before another
year was up I had pretty well cleaned out my stock
as listed in the catalogue. There were still millions
of plants on my grounds, in every possible stage of
development and every phase of progress; I couldn't
stop; I didn't want to; I went on producing new
varieties, and I went on calling them new creations,
and I still do, because I claim they were and are new
creations!

Plant improvement can only be done by a man
with a vision and a purpose. It is a lot like a man
who puts in a window and thinks he is an architect.
There is a wide gulf between the man who visions
and plans and supervises the building of a beautiful

structure and the man who drives the nails in its walls. Every nail is of importance, every window is of importance, but still somebody has to have all the general laws and principles and the whole idea in his mind. He has to adjust his building to its site, the materials to the surroundings, the workmen to the job, their needs to his purpose and their equipment and materials to their needs, and then, in the end, there emerges the architecture — the finished building — the thought completed that originated in the designer's mind.

In plant architecture, if I may coin an expression, the main thing that strikes me is that you have to wait for some of your materials to be arranged by Nature. Wild seeds are your raw material — wild seeds or cuttings from native trees or vines or shrubs: they are as wary and timid and hard to tame as wild animals, and also, as with wild animals, they are very likely to surprise you with traits and dispositions and tendencies you haven't counted on at all, so that you must be continually on your guard. Well, these raw materials and others you or some one before you have developed from them, must grow to your needs, while others you can arrange. You have certain materials at hand, but you have to wait for others — they partially arrange themselves. In ordinary architecture you merely shuffle them.

There is a good example of this in setting cement. You bring all your materials for the house or the business block or the public building together and plan your arrangement of them. You shuffle your brickwork and your woodwork and your doors and windows and your porches and balconies, and so on, to get them into the right places so that your final proportions and balance and mass will be right, but with all this, as soon as you start working, you have to wait for your cement to set before you can go on with your fine design. That is the way it is — that is precisely the way it is — with the work of the plant developer.

Some of my most important and valuable work has been with the plum. When I began, the plum was small, usually acid, generally unfit for shipping, often with a large stone, and sold in America in a limited number of varieties. I wanted to get a plum that would ship, a plum that would dry well — what we call a prune, because the French call it that — a plum that would be beautiful and delicious, a plum that would be large, a plum for canning, a plum with a small pit, or none at all, and so on. My designs were pretty carefully worked out.

For instance, as regards the shipping plum. The plum developed to be picked from the tree and eaten right there, or within a few hours in the house, was quite a different thing from the plum that could be picked, packed, shipped, delivered maybe thousands of miles away, unpacked, sold, carried home, and finally eaten fresh. You can see that. The variety for home consumption could be soft and juicy the minute it was ripe; the shipping plum had to be soft and juicy and delicious after it had traveled half as far as did Nelly Bly. And this couldn't be acquired by accident or chance — it had to be studied and the specifications pretty carefully written.

For shipping it was necessary to have the trees

bring their fruit to the proper stage of ripeness all at once. It would never pay an orchardist to go over and over his orchard, picking the plums that were ready and letting the others hang. Why, a man would starve to death with that sort of an orchard — his pickers would cost him more than his orchard was worth! You should be able to go right through the orchard, when the time came, and clean it up and cash in on the harvest.

Now you have a notion as to the ground-plan of just one plum. It was necessary to find parent stock that would contribute the proper blood-strains — one for firmness of flesh and juiciness, one, perhaps, for sturdiness in the tree, one for that characteristic of coming to perfection all at once. It was a case of choosing my materials carefully, then, by crossing, to get the beginnings of the building. But after that the scaffolding had to come away. I had to select and select and select for the qualities I was after, and it was a long and expensive job because a plum tree is not like some flowers — it will not take root and grow and bud and blossom and bear fruit all in a month or two, or even in several years; the short-cut I used, of course, was to bud well-established, sturdy trees with buds from the crossed seedlings I produced. Many men had worked at this, more or less; here is where I used the wholesale plan. Instead of trying one or two buds, or crossing for one or two results, or growing half a dozen seedlings, I would choose twenty varieties, grow fifty thousand seedlings, and bud hundreds of buds. More than that, I made my old parent trees work: sometimes I would bud as high as three hundred buds into one tree. It was new. It was startling to many. But it hurried Nature along. It brought results.

But not all at once, even then. By no means. Take the effort to get a stoneless plum. Remember that man can only utilize Nature's methods — he cannot alter or amend them. The man can plan the work, but he can't induce the plum to drop its stone all right away, even though man knows that, for his purposes, the stone is useless to the plum. You see, the plum has considered the stone important — about its most important part — through thousands and thousands of years, while man may have had the idea of dropping the stone for a few months. The wolf cannot be tamed in a minute because he has ten thousand years behind him that put a premium on his wildness.

There is no use trying to change everything in a day. Our environment — the influences brought to bear on us to change or alter or soften or harden us — what does it weigh? It weighs like a grain of sand, and heredity is untold and unknown accretions of grains of sand, added, added, added, mixed with the cement of time and custom and habit, and slowly changed into stone — almost imperishable stone, yet still susceptible of being taken by a competent quarryman and lifted from its place, and by a fine sculptor, with chisel and mallet, being transformed into something beautiful and majestic and immortal.

VII

A MAGAZINE writer who should have known better once put at the head of a story of my work and methods the title: 'Burbank versus Nature.' I can't remember anything that made me quite so hot under the collar as that caption. It was something like writing a treatise called: 'Wilbur and Orville Wright versus the Law of Gravitation.'

Because there never was a man lived on this planet who had more respect for Nature, who studied her rules and her system more diligently, nor whose work depended more on an understanding application of her laws. The newspaper headline writers long ago dubbed me 'The Plant Wizard,' and perhaps a good deal of nonsense has been written, at one time or another, along that general line. There was nothing mysterious, occult, magic, or metaphysical about my work — not in the slightest degree. I was Nature's pupil; I did manage to find ways to speed up her results, but wherever one of my experiments succeeded it was because I followed the rules, and where one failed, nine chances in ten it was because I overlooked some law or encountered a new section I hadn't committed to memory before.

Going to school to Nature, from my earliest days, I learned, first of all, that it was possible to direct the habits and tendencies of plants toward a greater usefulness and delight for mankind and also to release in them potentialities that were desirable from man's viewpoint. I have surprised many people by finding a striking parallel between plant and animal life; many have thought I was speaking figuratively when I have compared the education of plants to the education of children and, the other way about, have said that we can learn how to teach our children to their best advantage by observing carefully the laws Nature lays down for the development of plants and plant life.

There is, of course, a sensational similarity between the course of every kind and degree of life. Fundamentally the laws governing cells, or even crystals, are the same as those governing plant life, animal life, human life. All cells are made up of protoplasm which, in turn, is made up, as I have said before, of a little contribution from everything in Nature. How is it possible, then, that these cells, apparently of the same material and constituent elements, may grow into a flea or a buzzard, a crane or a horse, a pansy or a redwood tree, a bit of living scum on a stagnant stream or a beautiful child?

Well, a good figure there is the alphabet. There are twenty-six letters, and only part of them extensively used, yet there are something like half a million terms or words made up of those few letters — a handful. How? By different combinations. That is all. Some of the combinations are as violently and widely different as a toadstool and a lion are different — the first word in my dictionary is aabec and the last is zyxomma. Other words have a great similarity — benediction, benefaction, benefit, and benevolent, for example. Just a different train of cars, in each case, but all headed generally in the same direction. So, in living things, many of the or-

ganisms made up of cells have so much in common
that we group them together as distinct families,
such as the human family, with white men and red
men and black men — Saxons and Latins and Ne-
groes and Chinese, but all of them with eyes and ears
and mouths and legs and arms, walking erect and
being given the power to feel and reason and think
both backwards and forwards, and able to use their
thumbs, which, if you will consider it a minute, you
will find is one of the most remarkable differences
between man and the other animals, and the one
that makes possible most of man's handiwork and
the lack of which prevents the beasts from doing
more than the most elemental construction work.

The thing that binds all life together, then, is the
cell from which all life springs and of which all life is
made up. You cannot study plants without learning something about men, nor study men without
getting ideas about animals and fish and plants.
Comparatively few scientists speak in terms intelligible to the layman: they are specialists, concerned
with some particular phase or form of life, or with
determining laws governing particular activities,
developments, or manifestations of life. The naturalist, on the other hand, no matter how scientific,
makes himself understood by all because he deals
with a manifestation of life in which all are interested
and the language of which all the world speaks.
Plants and animals, forests and mountains, flowers
and children, are to be studied by any one; the naturalist only adds to the layman's understanding a
more extensive knowledge of the scientific basis for
those phenomena, actions and reactions, habits and

tendencies, mysteries and marvels, in which we are all interested and with which we are all more or less acquainted.

I am hoping that I will, therefore, be able to make myself as clear, in these papers, as though I were writing of salesmanship or how to drive an automobile — I want to talk the language of every day. In that tongue let us consider for a little this subject of Going to School to Nature.

I have told in an earlier chapter how my first helpful contact with Nature was when I came on a green spot of lush vegetation in the middle of a timber piece in New England in the dead of winter. That showed me that Nature had a provision by which plants could adjust themselves to an unusual or changed environment, and could not only thrive, but could pass on to succeeding generations this acquired power. In my earlier days as a truck gardener in Lunenburg I had forced corn to early harvest by planting the seed in hotbeds and crowding into the growing plant, when it was removed to the field, the food I knew it needed. This showed me that plants were amenable to improvement and speeding up, or to any other desired development, by the process of catering to their needs — by using the intelligence of man to take advantage of the general laws of life.

Those are examples of the lessons I learned in my chosen school very early. They were merely a suggestion of the infinite storehouse of information and knowledge Nature has for her children. As I went on with my work, instead of finding out everything and taking my degree and settling back with the feeling that I knew all that Nature had to teach, I discovered that everything I learned opened up new avenues for my ignorance; that every fact had a whole family of cousin-facts around it.

I began with the cell — the fundamental unit of life: it was apparent from all I saw that the cell was influenced by environment, that those influences, if they persisted long enough — repetition, repetition, repetition — entered into the heredity, and that this heredity was the factor I had most to deal with in training plants to bend themselves to man's greater good. Because it was the strongest factor and the deepest rooted; it was the one it had taken Nature generations and maybe centuries or ages to fix, and there was going to be no teaching these old dogs of the vegetable world the new tricks I had in mind for them to perform unless I used diligence, patience, and a knowledge of Nature's own processes.

In the potato I had had a striking lesson of the amazing variations that can come, suddenly, and without any apparent explanation, in the midst of the life of a common, unornamental, unsensational, everyday plant: I had proved that those variations could, by selection, be weeded out until the best was obtained. In other experiments, numerous and varied, I went farther and demonstrated that variations could be induced in plants, by cross-fertilization. There was my starting-point: the law that makes variations possible, and my ability to select from among the variations in order to get and fix the qualities desired.

It is one thing to know how a mathematical problem, for instance, is to be worked, and another to gather, place, and align all of a large number of factors in order to be ready for the actual figuring: it was so with my beginning in plant breeding. I have never left off studying; I have never felt that I came anywhere near mastering my subject; the learning was the greatest pleasure of my life, and still is, because Nature is not only a wise teacher, but she knows how to make her subjects fascinating, interesting, and full of marvel and beauty.

As I have said before, the raw material of the plant developer is the seed of the wild plant. This is true whether it is seed sought for and studied and sown for a definite or experimental purpose, as in my work, or is a seed brought home by an African bushman with a vague thought that it may add something to his store of edible plants. The wild growth of the world is the original parent stem — of all growth, and to the flowers and shrubs and vines and trees of our hills and mountains, prairies and deserts and plains, we turn for all our new sources of beauty and utility for our gardens and fields.

There was nothing so likely to attract the attention of the newcomer to California as the California poppy, that glorious golden-yellow flower that mantles all our hills and plains in the spring and that, with the purple lupin, goes to make landscapes incomparable in beauty — a revelation of the perfection with which Nature paints her scenes when she has a mind to exert herself a little. In the spring following my arrival in California I thought I should go mad with the excitement of watching those splendid carpets unroll on the hills around Santa Rosa; one would have supposed that I would weary of the poppies after a while, but I never have and never will. They were my first inspiration and delight, and from them I learned many of my most important early lessons.

I observed, among other things, that there was a wide variation in the poppy — both as between separate fields and in different localities, and also in the same fields, where there was more or less variation in size, color, and even, in some cases, in general formation. I found that some botanists classified the eschscholtzia (named for Johann Friedrich Eschscholtz, a German physician and naturalist who lived in the early part of the last century) as one single species, whereas others find twelve, Greene 112, and Fedde 123. They are all debating the matter, and from laboratory examination and analysis they have a right to be uncertain. But as a matter of fact the explanation is extremely simple. The California poppy is in a transitional stage — it has not yet found and fixed itself. To my way of thinking all the eschscholtzias that are actually California poppies are of the same species — a great family of brothers and sisters and cousins having a family resemblance, but with none of its characteristics definitely fixed. It is probably a young plant, botanically speaking, and hasn't found itself.

On the coast, for instance, the California poppy generally has a very large blossom — a different type from the inland poppy. As you come inland into the big valleys you find the blossoms growing darker in color, smaller, and more variable, probably from having migrated from different sides of the valley. You cross the valley, noting variations of

size and height, then, as you come up into the eastern foothills again, you get plants small in size and
somewhat smaller in blossom. It is when you begin
to climb toward the mountains themselves that the
greatest change is observable. No wonder the botanists call this mountain poppy a different species:
it bears a small, flat blossom, the plants hug the
ground closely, and any one who did not know better would certainly begin thinking up a new name
for a new species!

It took a long time, I found, to take this mountain
poppy back to big blossoms and plants again, even
with the most careful selection; it would take perhaps longer to get the valley poppies dwarfed down
to stand the high altitudes. But it could be done,
for I have done the same thing with other plants
and have impressed and impressed and impressed
them with what I was working for so repeatedly and
so patiently and so long that, in the end, they would
capitulate and give in and go to work for me as I
wanted them to work.

A most interesting study of these variations in
the poppy are found in a neighborhood north of
Santa Rosa, between the coast and the mountains,
where the soil varies in fifty feet in any given direction and where the climate is variable in a half-mile.
The altitude is fairly high, yet it is not mountain
country; on the other hand, the place cannot be
called lowland or a valley. There is a good deal of
moisture and so on. Well, the poor poppy has a
hard time to decide there what it is going to be, so it
compromises by being a little of everything!

That is what I mean. The difference in environ-

ment gave me there a more pliable plant — a plant
finely balanced — teetering on the edge, you might
say, and able to swing this way or that with far less
pressure from me than any plant, poppy or other,
that had grown set in its ways. Nature, you see,
helps the plant experimenter, more often than you
expect and with a more generous hand, especially
after you have the plant experiment started in the
right direction and have got rid of a lot of old, persistent, bigoted habits. In the case of these variegated poppies the unusual environment had already
caused the plants to shake off many of their fixed
ways and they were just ripe for change.

California plants, as a matter of fact, have so
many different climates, altitudes, moisture conditions, growing seasons, and so on, to deal with that,
as has been frequently pointed out to me by great
botanists, they show more variations in themselves
than plants almost anywhere in the world. Also,
of course, this fact gave me another advantage,
namely, that I could grow in my gardens plants from
all over the world — a larger percentage of the
known plants, perhaps, than most plant experimenters could study and work with. There are
many — thousands and thousands — that will not
live, even in California, but my field was broader
than it would have been pretty nearly anywhere else.

Here, then, was one of my lessons from Nature —
that different environments produce plants of the
same family that are so widely different that even
the botanists want to put them into separate classifications, and yet they are the same plants identi-
cally. Their only differences were the pure result of

environment, and expressed themselves physically, in varying shades, shapes, sizes, and so on, without being in the least different in their actual make-up or heredity. It is a crystal-clear illustration of the natural law which, intelligently applied by man, with a definite purpose in his mind, would eventuate in new forms — in what I call *new creations*.

The poppy is an example of the variations caused by varying climatic, moisture, and soil conditions, and by altitude; there are other variations in plants that are due to environmental conditions which modify the plant or its structure or its habits to fit it to receive help from friendly surroundings and to ward off injury from unfriendly ones. Forget everything, for example, but the leaves of plants and trees. Notice those in your garden or a park or along the streets, or in the country. No two just alike! So different in shape and form and thickness and texture and length and position on the tree or the plant or the twig or the stalk as hardly to be the same sort of thing. Why?

Always there is a cause, if not in the present history of the plant, then sometime in its past history. Nothing about a plant or an animal or a human being exists by chance — Nature may select by chance or she may develop an unexpected and apparently accidental characteristic, but if you look far enough you will always find that everything about a plant or an animal is the result of the working of some clear law. And so there is a cause for the leaf — its shape and form and texture, and I know of nothing more interesting than to speculate on that cause and to determine it if you can.

The needle-like leaf of the pine, for example, is the result of the need the pine had for sunshine bathing it, in the comparatively short season that it lives in the sun, and of the need the tree had to shed the great loads of snow that fall on it in winter-time. If it had had a leaf like the banana palm, how long would the pine have lasted under a two-foot fall of snow? Also it is a tough leaf — take two or three green needles in your hand and twist and pull them and you will see they will stand pretty rough usage. Well, there is the leaf to bear up under driving wind and pelting rain and heavy snow and cold and even the intense midsummer heat of the mountain-home of the pine.

The banana leaf is exactly opposite — broad, tender, casting a great shade, catching whatever moisture there is for it to catch, and never having to bear up against wind or snow. Go on to the desert and there examine the leaves of the native growth. You could not expect to find a thin, delicate leaf on any desert that had been desert long, because of the sandstorms, the terrific heat, and the lack of moisture. So you find tough, pachydermic skin, like that of the elephant, or else covered with fine hairs or some substance to protect it. What we call the ice-plant, that grows along the coasts, has a tough skin on its leaves and it grows low and sprawling because of the wind and the sharp sand blown against it by the wind. There is not a single plant or tree that does not have an absorbing story in its leaf structure, if you will take the pains to study it.

Now there is something from Nature's book worth learning! The rosebush is covered with thorns, the

porcupine with spines, the cactus with poison darts
— and all for the same purpose: defense. The strawberry hides under its broad leaves, the rabbit under
a bush, and both because they have no other protection except to avoid being seen by enemies. The
fruit pit, bearing the seed, it is very difficult to
break into; the soles of a man's feet are tough and of
thickened skin; in each case the reason is, originally,
that the seed must be housed against destruction by
birds, the feet armored against thorns and pebbles
and a nail in the shoe! Do you think these natural
provisions are the result of chance?

Not at all. There is a dispute among scientists as
to the exact method by which these provisions are
ultimately bred into the individual, but there is no
dispute as to the purpose. It is to preserve life and
to make it possible for that life to re-create itself
in offspring — the two cardinal laws of being in the
world. And you can easily apply the law in more
ways than one in your everyday existence. Taking a
leaf from Nature's book you can teach yourself to
be superior to exterior aggravations, troubles, and
annoyances; you can build yourself an armor against
sickness and failure; you can adjust yourself to your
environment, or, if you find that impossible or undesirable, you can seek a new environment and
adapt yourself to that, for your own ends. Mind
may or may not be everything and matter nothing
— I can hardly subscribe to that doctrine! — but
there is no question that Mind, trained, directed,
educated, can school and guide the body, on the one
hand, and use or discard, capitalize or ignore, material things pressing upon it — can, in short, adjust
itself to environment!

VIII

IN the previous chapter I referred to the dispute among scientists as to the procedure by which adjustments are made by plants and animals so that new powers and abilities and even new muscles, members, or whole organs come into being and are incorporated in the heredity of that variety, or, on the other hand, are slowly dropped from that heredity and cease to be known there. For example, the heron must have been once a short-legged bird; the horse was once an animal as big as a dog and had toes; man's ancient ancestors were from the same parent stock as apes and, in the dim ages of the past, had a tail and swung from trees. What lengthened those legs, or changed the horse's toes to a hard but springy hoof, or curtailed your friends and acquaintances?

There is a very interesting theory, supported by some of the facts before us and apparently denied by others, that is called the theory of 'use and disuse'; that theory holds that when need creates a certain kind of leaf, for instance, in a plant, that certain kind of leaf persists as long as the need for it exists, that is, as long as it is *used;* it goes on to the corollary proposition that, if the need ceases to exist and that certain kind of leaf is no longer used, it will eventually cease to exist and the plant will have another kind of leaf.

This theory of 'use and disuse' leads us to another theory of biologists, namely, that need can create a function in an animal or a plant, and that function can and does create an organ to take care of it. As an illustration we may take the time when certain sea-animals came out to live on the land, as they did centuries and centuries ago. In the sea they need gills to breathe through and fins to swim with. On land they breathed without gills; they swam no longer, but instead they walked and needed legs and feet, and their fins were useless to them. The *need* of legs, these theorists maintain, was apparent before the actual legs were; the need created the *function* of walking; the function of walking brought about the *structure* with which to walk, that is, the legs. You will find scientists who deny this theory, but my work demonstrated its truth to me beyond any questioning or doubt.

You can put it down as a very good rule, the structural always follows the functional; in other words, the necessity of a thing is exhibited as functional and afterward the structure arises. Structure — the shape of the pine leaf, for instance — is built up by function — the need to shed snow, in the pine leaf, and to stand wind, let us say; and the function or power to shed snow is upheld by structure, that is, the long needle-shaped pine leaf. In plants most all their functions are taken care of by temporary structures: if the need of the structure disappears the structure disappears too. It is like the staging or scaffolding on a building — it is absolutely essential to the process of erection, but once the building is standing firmly the scaffolding comes down and can be used in the interior of the building somewhere, perhaps. Often, as a matter of fact, the plant actually does use its staging for some other purpose, and always the strength that went into the staging goes later into the plant.

Let us take an example of this need bringing about a function and function bringing about a structure or organ or ability to meet the necessities of the case. Here is a man. He is a fighter — a warrior — pugnacious, because he once lived in tribes and had to fight for food and for a wife and for his chance — had to fight for elbow-room, even. He lived that way for centuries. Civilization came, we invented policemen to guard us against thieves, we trained dogs to protect us against tramps, we instituted laws to protect us against greedy or turbulent or dishonest neighbors, and we built up armies and navies to prevent other tribes from coming in and enslaving us.

The fighting spirit in man became almost unnecessary so that most of us now live peaceably and quietly and we don't go out and knock a man down to take his beef away from him or his wheat or his wool — we go into a store and pay him for those things. The strength and nervous force and skill required for fighting in the ages gone are now directed to other needs we have and we build ships and skyscrapers, we write books and poems, we invent aëroplanes and discover vitamins, and breed plants.

Here is a plant — the horseradish. Originally it put a lot of its strength into seed — and do not forget that the growing of seed takes a tremendous amount of sap and food and vital energy from every plant; but people more and more raised it from tubers so that, finally, the horseradish practically ceased to produce seed. That is true also of the potato; it is only once in a long time that you find a potato seed-ball. There are plenty of examples, too, among plants that were originally climbers. They had to climb up to get sun or air or rain, but after a while they grew strong, were able to take care of themselves, and they lost the habit of climbing and eventually lost the ability to climb.

You see, when you force a plant, or when Nature or necessity forces a plant, to do something that is unusual or difficult for it to do, it will do it, if it can, but the effort costs it too much. It takes more vital force for a woman to run to catch a train than she can afford to spend; after a while perhaps she decides she will take a later train — or else she starts early so she will make connections without running herself half to death! The plant finds it takes too much strength to adjust itself to an unfriendly environment with just the old equipment it started with — equipment that it had in an earlier and more friendly environment. There is the need, then there is the function, then, after a time, the plant builds up a structure to perform that function and take care of that need automatically. There is the same thing again that I have spoken of so often in my work: repetition, repetition, repetition, of need eventually gives the plant a new machinery for taking care of the need, and the new machinery becomes a part of the regular equipment of the plant's factory, and that improved equipment becomes a part of the plant's heredity.

Precisely the same thing occurs in humans. A great many teachers and parents use repetition,

repetition, repetition, in training children; though they may not know it they are fixing in those children something that, if it goes on for enough generations, will become a part of the child, and will be passed on by that child to its children. It is not necessarily the words that fix themselves in the minds of children so much as circumstances and incidents and experience that fix impressions in the mind. Repetition makes those impressions stronger and stronger, the human mind reacts to these impressions with a new function or power to take care of the new impressions or needs or desires, the new function or power builds up a structure, perhaps in the brain, so that finally the structure takes care of the need automatically and the structure saves so much by this special adaptability to a special use that it becomes transmissible. That is where our heredities come from — from experiences and needs and desires and habits long and long known to us and long and long met with our best efforts. Heredity is nothing but stored environment — the sum of all our past environments. I have said that before: I cannot say it too often.

There was another of the great lessons I learned in Nature's school. When I went to work with a plant I first considered its heredity. I knew that it was used to a certain climate, a certain cultural method, a certain soil, and that it was in the habit of delivering a certain sort of crop for value received. I learned how strong heredity is in all life, and that you could not hope to overcome an old heredity with new influences in a short time unless by a short-cut method that would take advantage of that old heredity rather than attempt to turn it suddenly into a new channel.

I had to be sure of my groundwork — the plant's heredity — before I could make a start with improving it, or experimenting with it. In the first place, heredity governs more strictly as regards the climate than as regards any other thing in a plant or tree. Lots of time has been wasted trying to make cold-country plants adapt themselves to hot countries, and plants from the tropics thrive in a temperate or colder zone. There is one possible way to overcome this hereditary obstinacy, and that is to take a plant from a hot country, find a cousin of the plant that grows in a cold country, and cross them, and from the cross you would get seedlings, one out of a thousand of which might give you the desired adaptability to the new climate. But the problem is to find relatives from common origins that have become this much scattered over the world.

You know by its heredity pretty much where any fruit tree will thrive, if it is not too much crossed and its heredity jumbled. So long as you can trace out its main heredity you are all right. The Concord grape is an Eastern American and thrives over a good part of the United States and the southern Canadian lands. The European grapes were originally Asiatic; they have been longer under cultivation and their ways are more fixed and set, therefore they demand certain things of their climate and soil, and do better in semi-tropical climates. In my work I have studied such factors so long that I can tell more easily about the life story of a plant, even a stranger to me, if I know where it comes from, than most people can, but the study is interesting enough for any one, and can take you all around the globe, almost, in your own garden.

Now here is another thing that I learned going to Nature's school: that plants have as many qualities and characteristics and peculiarities, pretty nearly, as a human being, and your handling of them has to be determined by the length of time those qualities, characteristics, or peculiarities have been in the heredity of the individual plant. Let me go into that a little carefully.

All living things, as I see it, have three powers inherent in them: the power to fight for their self-preservation, the power to re-create themselves in progeny, whether by spawning, seeding, breeding, or the mating of humans, and finally — and this is a different way of putting it from that you will find generally in the textbooks! — the power to vary.

Throughout all Nature the most cunning and sometimes intricate machinery is provided by the individual itself, or by Nature for the individual, if you please, through which it can protect itself from its enemies and take advantage of the help of its friends. The lion is powerful enough to defend himself; the tortoise is slow and helpless, so he has a thick shell to armor him against his foes. The eagle is swift and strong; the rabbit can dart into a low covert where he finds asylum. The blackberry grows in high, open, showy fashion, where any marauder can rob it of its fruits, which contain its seeds, so it was furnished with a multitude of sharp thorns; the strawberry, on the other hand, grows low, hides its fruits with its leaves, and is unostentatious and modest enough to escape any but the sharpest eyes. And so through all Nature.

That is the power to preserve itself, *in the individual*.

Of what use self-preservation to the whole scheme of things, though, unless the species could be carried on? Nature does not heed nor give thought to the individual; she is ruthless and even, we are compelled to think, sometimes cruel and merciless, as far as the single animal or plant is concerned, but she seems to be intent on the whole organization — on life in its broad, permanent, and universal significance. If the scheme for the preservation of any single individual fails, either through the failure of that individual or through the activity of enemies, Nature is determined that the species shall go on. Even where a species is wiped out, it almost never fails that something of that species has gone into another, or else that a new one takes its place. Life as a whole continues, and that appears to be the natural law of which we can be most infallibly certain.

Therefore the second natural law makes possible — makes even inevitable, one would say — the reproduction of life. In animals a delicate mingling of the sense and nerves with the sexual organs brings about mating; in plants the equipment seems even more marvelous and cunning to us. I am going to go later into the elaborate and beautiful devices by which flowers, for instance, attract bees, insects, or birds to themselves in order to get those living things to work for them in carrying their pollen from one to another; also into the fabulous provisions

made in the individual flowers to fertilize their seeds.
For the moment we can pass, too, the artful means
provided by which seed is distributed: the pea grown
round so that it will roll; the seed of the thistle attached to a parachute of down that will carry it for
long distances; many weeds, like the devil's-claw,
with seeds in pods or containers which have sharp
fangs to fasten into the hoof or tail or coat of a
passing animal and thus obtain a sort of blind-
baggage ticket to some far-away destination. It is
in such themes as this that the student in Nature's
school grows garrulous and enthusiastic!

Now! The power to fight for self-preservation and
the power to re-create itself are in every living
organism: the third power is the power to vary.

I have already spoken about the influence on
heredity that is brought in by the mother, in the
human family: the two sexes always contribute that
result, but it is, nevertheless, a part of the variation
of which I am now speaking. On top of that, and of
the utmost importance to the plant breeder in his
work, there is the power in the plant to adjust itself
to environment and adapt itself to changed conditions. There is a third cause of variation in life —
the addition of characteristics formerly undis-
covered and unknown in a strain — and this cause
Hugo de Vries calls mutation: that is the sudden
and unexpected appearance, in the form of a sport
or mutant, of a new characteristic or even a new
form in an individual. But in each case these variations may be accounted for, in so far as they register
themselves in the individual, and, if impressed there
by repetition, become fixed in the heredity passed on

to succeeding generations, by the presence in Nature of the power to vary.

If there were no such power in the plant it would be a definite, limited thing from the beginning of time to the end; instead we find animals and plants and men constantly changing, acquiring new powers, taking on new attributes, developing new possibilities, and making the steady progress we must see in all of life. I do not mean that these variations in plants are always beneficial to the plant, or that they always result in what any one, from any point of view, could call an improvement. Thousands and millions of plants have varied and, as a result, have died. But when the variation produces an added power, or the adjustment or adaptation is to meet an inimical influence or condition, the plant becomes that much stronger and better suited to its environment, and therefore makes what all must recognize as progress, certainly *as far as the plant itself is concerned*. My task was to take advantage of this power to vary and, using it, to produce, as far as I could, a plant that was improved *from the viewpoint of man*. The law was the same, the process was the same, and often the purpose was the same, but not always. For instance, solely from the point of view of the plum tree, it might be far more desirable for it to produce seed — in its stone — always; from man's point of view it would be better to have a stoneless plum, and I produced one.

All this has been entered into to tell you something of the last great lesson I learned in Nature's school: namely, that the oldest and most fixed characteristics of a plant were the ones hardest to change and most stubborn to deal with, and that what had been added to the plant — to its heredity — in the long processes of time were easier to influence and change in direct proportion to the length of time the plant had manifested those characteristics. For example, the most fixed and inflexible characteristic of a tree is to fight for existence and to re-create itself; later it learned to vary; later it learned to grow a fine protective spread of foliage to protect itself; later, perhaps, it learned to give its fruit a certain amount of sugar over and above the amount needed to protect its stone, or pit, properly; later, we'll say, it learned to color its fruit, and so on.

It came to the place, in the end, where the plant had developed what I can almost call an artistic temperament — a response to demands for beauty and flavor and odor and so on. Most fruits, even in their wild state, have some beauty or flavor or aroma in blossoms or fruit — partly put there to attract bees and birds to help in pollinization or the dissemination of seeds, but also partly, I think, in answer to the universal urge of beauty in our universe. And those last additions to the plant were the easiest to influence when they came to my experiment gardens.

You might say that, of the æsthetic inclinations in fruit trees, the first is toward perfume in the blossom, then aroma or bouquet in the fruit itself, then flavor, then what we call quality — that is, the texture of the flesh, the thinness of the skin, the content of sugar, the value as nourishment, and so on. The most æsthetic qualities in a fruit are scarcely sensed by many people; it takes an epicure to sense

a high and juicy flavor or aroma or fragrance, just
as a large number of people are not able even to
catch the evanescent colors or tones in music, or
overtones, because they themselves have not been
developed up to it. Environment has not yet produced in them the last, delicate perceptions that are
possible to them, you see.

Luckily I could get many variations in plants by
crossing two, each of which had one or more characteristics necessary to my purpose, as hardiness,
generous bearing of blossoms or fruit, early or late
fruiting, or what-not. And combining heredities, by
cross-pollinization, and thereafter selecting those
individuals showing the strongest tendency toward
my purpose, was one of the chiefest methods in my
repertoire. It was here that there entered the one
important process I relied on and which I had never
seen stressed by any one before me — the repetition,
repetition, repetition, of one influence on one plant
for one purpose, time after time, day after day,
generation after generation, patiently, tirelessly,
without ever changing my idea or deviating from my
plain course, until, in the end, the characteristic or
quality or power I wanted in the plant was so firmly
fixed in it — in its heredity, you see, even though it
was the very latest and newest part of that heredity
— that it could no more be bred out or dropped out
or lost than could the plant's tendency to send its
roots downward and its leaves upward!

These are some of the lessons I learned in going
to school to Nature. Not all of them, by any means;
not perhaps the most striking, new, or exciting of the
lessons, but the ones that were fundamental and

therefore most vital to my work in life. Even with these lessons learned I did not find it easy always to achieve my end — to lead or urge or tease or drive the plant into my way of thinking. Sometimes Nature seemed to throw my reward right into my lap; at other times I made an effort time and again, time and again, and grew almost discouraged. But then, perhaps, I would say to myself, 'Well, I'll stay with it another year,' and I would, and one day, without a bit of warning, there would be my long-hoped-for result jumping out at me the whole length of a row!

I do not envy any man living! I have never heard of any work or occupation or vocation that seems to me to rival that of the scientist, especially of the scientist who is equally a humanist and whose research and study and experiments and discoveries are all directed to the end that man may find this old sphere a better and more beautiful place in which to live. After all, every scientist is adding something to this result, no matter whether his work seems closely related to human needs and desires or not. For what you may think of, in scientific work, as useless, like the search for the North Pole or the naming of a new species of fish, is really a contribution to our knowledge, and knowledge is power — and a power that, sooner or later, will be needed and can be turned into the dynamo to give added possibilities to life.

Yes, I have long seen that each grain of knowledge I acquired, going to school to Nature, was added to each other grain I possessed, that these grains grew into a foundation stone, that the stones accumulated until I had a substructure, and that on the sub-structure I could build me a house. And I have seen, too, that there are enough buildings in Nature's system of knowledge to make a great city of wisdom.

I will never see that city completed: no man will. At best he may be able to construct, during his life-time, one or two buildings, and perhaps to catch a vision of a few streets and squares and parks and pre-cincts of the whole. But the sublimity of the city — its endless boulevards, its imposing monuments, its transcendent capitol, its towering edifices, its vistas and sweeping panoramas — these we can only imagine, from the view we get of the structures of knowledge we ourselves are able to build up, grain by grain, rock by rock, tier by tier, story by story, through diligence and hard work, into one or two of the buildings we know are all there, somewhere, to be builded. When I think of this, I wonder why some men are content to erect nothing more than rude huts of knowledge — a little cabin of selfish learning, enough to house them while they amass money or gain power or win fame — and will not even try to raise some nobler structure of the wis-dom Nature offers so freely and generously, and that any who come to her may have for the asking!

IX

PROBABLY I was the first man who ever lived to take a specific order for a new variety of plant or tree, and to deliver that order as definitely as a contractor, taking an architect's blue-prints, will deliver a sky-scraper or a church, a cottage or a mansion.

A good many people have not understood this; I know that it is sometimes supposed that my experiments have been performed by following along favorable lines of development, more or less accidental or fortuitous, until, by chance and some skill in selection, I have produced a new variety of plum or poppy or gladiolus. On the contrary, while many such accidental developments have occurred and have been taken advantage of, most of my work has been toward a definite and exact result, and I have persisted in my pursuit of this fixed purpose until I have achieved it.

I mention this here, and want to go on to write specifically of methods and results, because, in this work of plant development there lies before the young men of to-day a field of research and invention so important and so rich in possibilities that I can see no limits or boundaries to it. It is a field almost neglected, yet in it are found promises of a service to mankind compared with which mechanical invention and the discovery and exploitation of new manufacturing processes fade into shadows. What Edison and Ford and the Wright brothers and Alexander Bell and Marconi and his followers and all the other great geniuses of chemistry and mechanics have achieved for the world is to be equaled if not surpassed, in time, by the men who turn their attention to the plant world and there harness the unimaginable powers and direct the illimitable potentialities that exist and that only need guiding or releasing to double the working capital of the world.

I have said before that it was a well-meant but inaccurate thought that gave me the name of 'The Plant Wizard'; I have a gift or special ability or what folks call a genius for selection, but there is nothing magical or mysterious about my methods, and what I learned to do others can learn to do, and what I have started others can finish, and what I have found out about the laws of Nature in this connection can be applied by others and added to by others, if only they will waken to the possibilities that exist. I studied Nature, I codified her laws, I applied them to get practical and valuable results, and I think of myself, not at all as a Master whose work must die with him, but as a Pioneer who has mapped out certain new roads and looked down into the Promised Land of plant development.

From thousands of incidents let me choose one to show how exact (in practice, provided you have patience and industry and knowledge of your ground) can be the filling of orders in plant development. A Western canner, one of my best friends, is Mr. John H. Empson. He came to me one day a good many years ago, and told me that there would be a great market for a small, sweet, succulent garden pea for canning. The canned French pea had long been a familiar commodity to grocers and consumers, but it was high in price and Mr. Empson was convinced that an American product could be made that would equal it in every respect.

'Do you think such a pea might be developed?' Mr. Empson asked.

'Certainly,' I said. 'Will you order it from me?'

He laughed. 'I can tell you that, if you happen to get such a pea, I can get growers to specialize in it to great advantage. If I thought you could accept a definite order and deliver a definite product, I would be glad to place such an order, but that is impossible, of course.'

'Not at all,' I said. 'I know what you want, and I will deliver it to you inside of eight years, perhaps less.'

I knew then, and Mr. Empson told me afterward, that he couldn't quite believe I was serious. But I was entirely serious because I had given myself definite orders in hundreds of cases and delivered on practically all of them. Moreover, this garden-pea order was comparatively simple.

The French pea is actually a pea that is not allowed to come to full maturity, but that is picked, by hand, when the peas in the pod have reached their most perfect state as regards flavor and sweetness. You see, as in most vegetables, the sugar content in the pea begins, as the time of ripening passes, to turn into starch, in which form it is stored for use in feeding the life-germ when the pea is planted and germinates. If you pick your pea before that turning-point is reached, the pea is sweet and deliciously flavored, though not yet at its full size.

My first problem was to develop a pea that would be well formed, firm, and of uniform size when it was still not entirely matured, and it was there that I started. I chose good, uniform peas for planting, and I planted a large field of them. By selection I found individual plants with a tendency toward the sort of qualities I wanted; the chosen pods were carefully saved and replanted, and selection again made toward the ideal.

Meantime there was another vital requisite in these peas. It was all well enough for the French to pick their peas by hand for canning, because they could work cheaply and charge high prices; for California canners it was necessary to have peas that would reach the desired size and have the desired qualities almost simultaneously over a whole field — in short, the peas must be so characterized that they could be harvested by machinery, perhaps in one or two days. This meant that I must also select and reselect to get uniformity of ripening period.

My process was simple enough, but it required the application of infinite pains and patience. For instance, as the plan progressed, I harvested my selected seed only after counting the separate pods on each vine and the separate peas in each pod, choosing between vines otherwise alike in product, according to the quantity as well as the quality of the peas. The promise had been made that I would make delivery within eight years; as a matter of fact California conditions enabled me to plant two generations each year and in six generations, or at the end of three years, I sent for Mr. Empson and told him his pea was perfected.

He was amazed and sincerely delighted. In the course of this work we had become well acquainted and very friendly; I refused to let him pay me, of course, because of this friendship, and turned the pea-seed stock over to him to use for his own purposes. The pea was called the Burbank Empson, and to-day it is one of the chief crops in a large community in this State. Here was a definite order, definitely fulfilled, five years earlier than had been promised, but it was not magical nor mysterious. It was simply an application of the laws of Nature as expressed in plant life, but that run through all life. It is an excellent, though small, example of what I mean above when I say that this field of endeavor is wide open to young men and women, and that, while the rewards may be meager because as yet there is no method by which the plant inventor is protected in the rights to his invention, will pay enormous returns in satisfaction and incalculable returns in the good of the race.

There are four divisions into which this almost untouched work may be divided: improving the quality of fruits and vegetables and the beauty and fragrance of flowers; second, adapting plants to new environments and increasing the range of climates, soil conditions, and so on, in which they will thrive and bear; third, developing plants so that they will, because of characteristics and strengths impressed on their present heredities, waste less time and vital force, and therefore have more of both with which to increase their yields; and fourth, developing wild plants now unknown or unused by man into useful and valuable servants and friends.

It requires but a moment's consideration to see how true this is. As I have previously pointed out, nearly everything we eat and wear and a great deal of what we use in everyday life comes to us primarily through the leaves of plants. The mineral world, important as it is to man, contributes less to his comfort and development than the animal and vegetable worlds, and of these, the former, if you trace back far enough, is dependent on the second. So that the principal source of man's wealth, health, pleasure, and happiness is the plant life of this planet! If that is true, it must be plain that in neglecting study and culture and invention and creation in this realm we are defrauding ourselves of untold billions of wealth and untold measures of satisfaction, beauty, and utility.

I have spent a lifetime scratching at the surface of this illimitable field; out of more than one hundred thousand separate, costly, and often bold experiments I have added more than I can count in numbers and more than I can estimate in value — new wealth — to the gardens, fields, and orchards of the world. This is not written boastfully, but in the hope of encouraging others to enter this poorly explored and sketchily mapped territory of applied science. If I could stir even half a dozen young men or women (for it is a field in which women could compete with an equal chance and equal credit and equal achievements with men), I would feel that I had done even more than I have thus far in actual creations and discoveries. The joy of the pathfinder and explorer is much more in seeing settled and cultivated the wilderness he discovers than in the initial discovery itself.

Of all my developments probably that best known and the results of which are most widely distributed and capitalized on by growers is my development of the plum. And nothing could give a clearer idea of how all my work was done and how results were made possible than by telling you something of the history of my experiments with this fruit. There are many other trees and flowers in which I have met with greater difficulties, from which I have learned more, and which have given me greater personal satisfaction, but the widest application in practice has, thus far, been made of the large variety of plums I have produced. Let us go back to the beginning of this fruit tree, then, and trace the steps of the work, in order that you may understand what plant development means and how it is achieved.

Almost anywhere in the United States you can find, in wild, natural state, at least scattered members of the wild-plum family of trees. We have no definite way of knowing where the plum originated, but probably it was in that interesting and ancient triangle roughly pointed by the Caspian and Mediterranean Seas and the Persian Gulf to which scientists trace many of our plants and animals and somewhere near which, it is possible, the human race itself had its beginnings. The plum became widely scattered, though, and this is not surprising when you consider its beautiful color, its firm flesh, its unique flavor, even in the wild state, and its hardiness, both of seed and tree. It could stand transporting over greater distances than the peach, the cherry, the pear, for instance, and it had in it the power to vary to adapt itself to new climates and soils; it was tempting to birds and animals and to man, and they carried it about, either merely for the sake of eating it, or for the sake, as in the case of ancient tribes, of planting it and cultivating it for use.

Certainly it is found pretty much all over the world, and though the records of diligent investiga-tors fail to show that it was a familiar fruit in an-cient times, it must have been one that barbarous peoples ate, since only they could have carried and dispersed its seeds so widely. And this is interesting and important because it shows that the vitality and adaptability of the plum make it available for de-velopment so that it can be raised, eventually, al-most everywhere where any deciduous trees will live.

On the other hand, the plum, forced through ages to protect its life-germ, in the seed, from animals, developed a stone, or pit, that was large, very strong, and greatly exacting from the tree. I have said several times that the making of pit-fiber and the nut or seed of any plant is the task that puts the heaviest load on that plant: it takes perhaps from five to ten times as much strength and nourishment for a plum tree to make its pits and seeds as it does for it to spread new leaf or root growth or to develop its blossoms. Therefore the plum had less strength to give to fruit, and the result was a tree with a small, acid fruit and a large, very strong pit about the seed.

Perhaps it has not occurred to you that the build-ing of railroads and the erection of drying-plants and canneries marked a new era in the race-history of plants, but it is true. What we speak of as orchards, especially in large fruit-growing sections, are new developments that were brought into being by modern invention — the improvement of methods of transportation and the working-out of plans for extensive drying and canning operations. Originally all fruits were wild; there was a long, dark era in their race-histories when they grew merely for the purpose of perpetuating themselves through blossoms to attract birds and insects to help in the process of pollinization, through fruits to tempt birds and animals to disseminate them widely, and through the protective pit and the fertile seed or kernel.

The pulp or flesh of the fruit, originally designed only as advertising, to attract customers who would help scatter the seed, fulfilled its purpose and did it in a very perfect and complete way, for eventually men began to value the fruits so much that they not only transported the seeds but they planted them, tenderly cared for the young seedlings, pruned and cultivated the mature trees, and introduced a new era into the race-history of fruits — the age of gardens. For a long, long time, considered from the viewpoint of human beings, fruit trees were made a part of every garden, so that the owner had fruit for himself and his family. The word would go around the neighborhood, too, that Ak or Boris or Amos had a new treat in his garden, and he would find plenty of local customers to help him eat his plums or pomegranates or figs. But even if he went into business he could not reach a market very far from home, because, in the first place, he had no means of rapid transportation and, in the second, the fruit would not stand handling nor last long before it had to be eaten. The era of the fruit-garden, where the consumption was purely home consumption, was the second in the race-history of the fruit.

It was discovered that certain fruits, notably figs and dates, could be dried and in that condition carried over long distances and kept for months in good shape, and a certain amount of business was done in the dried-fruit industry. But nothing to speak of, considered in a broad way, until, within my own time, the steam engine and the steel mill made possible the railroad. The third era in the history of the race of fruit trees of the world is the era of transportation and modern packing methods.

It was in my time, too — it was not more than a few decades since — that consumers showed that they would pay high prices for fresh fruit, preferring it to canned goods or dried fruits. I saw that this would be true, but I was one of the first — in fact, for a time, I was the only man devoting study and experiment to the end that fruits might be developed that would stand transportation and arrive in the hands of distant consumers in attractive condition. It was here that I began my work with plums.

I must recall to your minds what I have said previously about the two new ideas that went into my life-work: the idea that a man could use Nature's own processes in a wholesale and definitely planned way, and the idea that he could considerably speed up her processes. There is no clearer illustration of this than to compare the fashion by which Nature worked before man entered into the field at all, and the methods he used and the results he got, even in the most slipshod and indefinite style, after he began to raise fruit. It took the wild plum uncounted thousands of years to develop into the small, sour, undesirable fruit we find in our own woods and canyons to-day; in two or three short centuries, with nothing more than the most casual knowledge or care, man made the plum edible, fairly sweet, and measurably juicy by untrained selection and by cultivation. But he did not work by wholesale and he did not work with any definite purpose or any single-minded enthusiasm.

I brought both to the task.

At the time I came to California there were three varieties of plums grown here, one of which was of very little use at all, and neither of the other two of which would stand shipping. About 1880 I was beginning to turn my thoughts more and more toward experiments wholly; the nursery business was growing and profitable, but it seemed to me most anybody could conduct a nursery and it wasn't everybody who would (even if he could) carry on the extensive experiments in plant development that I was itching to get at. Of course I would have to make my experiments pay, somehow, or I would soon be up a tree; the nursery business had shown me that fruits were going to be in great demand in California, and, casting about for one that needed attention and showed inherent possibilities, I lighted on the plum.

At about this same time, with my mind alert to pick up any vibrations that keyed in with my slowly formulating plans, I was browsing in the

Mechanics Library in San Francisco when I came across a book written by an American sailor about his wanderings in Japan, and in it there was a description of a 'blood-red' plum found in the province of Satsuma. That sailorman was not a skilled writer, but he certainly must have been a good trencherman, because he described that plum so that it made your mouth water to read about it! As far as I was concerned the red-fleshed plum of Satsuma was sold and the first payment made down! I was going to have it for California.

Of course I had neither time nor money to go to Japan, but I knew of a bulb dealer, Isaac Bunting, an Englishman, in Yokohama, and when I was in shape to start the plum experiments I sent to him and asked him to send me a dozen seedlings of Japanese plums. The first shipment arrived in the fall of 1884, but they were all dead! So, continuing some simple experiments I was performing with local plums, I wrote to Mr. Bunting again and on December 20, 1885, I received what was probably the most important single importation of fruit trees ever delivered in America — twelve sturdy, healthy Japanese plum seedlings, among them one of the variety my sailorman had described.

The Japanese, an island people, closely hemmed in by their environment, you might say, and strongly impressed by it, impress on all their products their own tastes and likes; on the plum, as they raised it, were impressed bright color, succulence, prolific bearing, and a tree-habit of sturdiness combined with that crude, irregular form which so appeals to the Japanese. Behind their plums was all the wild-tree heredity running back through thousands of years, no doubt, and on that had been superimposed the other hereditary traits that had come to their plums through environment and their own selection.

I do not think that, in the sense in which I judge plant improvement, the Japanese went deliberately about this work of making the plum characteristically Japanese. They had the seedlings, and when a good one came along, they passed it around among the neighbors and so it got a foothold. Repetition, repetition, repetition, put into the plum the habits and characteristics the people preferred, so that it mirrors them, in a way, and is marked with their trademark, for me, as clearly as though it were stamped: 'Made in Japan.'

And two points are interesting here. The individuals in the Caucasian race are made up of such a number of world races that we get a greater variety of tastes among them. Some like a sweet fruit, some a sour, some a soft, mellow texture, some a crisp, firm one, and so on. Orientals are a less mixed race, therefore they have tastes in food and fruits more in common. The second point is that wherever you find cultivated leisure classes you will find a varied and complex diet, whereas a race largely made up of the peasant or lower class, with few nobles or higher-class people for them to know about and study and imitate, will have generally a coarse, simple fare and fruits, for instance, located inside a narrow range of flavors, textures, and so on. The Japanese are, though, an æsthetic people, and this crops out in their fruit because all their fruits and their flowers are remarkable for beauty.

The twelve seedlings Mr. Bunting had sent me went right to work, and from them I added considerably to my store of knowledge of the secrets of Nature as regards variation in plants. I was fairly familiar with the tree habits of the Japanese plum, from reading and from pictures; it amazed me to see how my seedlings took hold and how quickly they showed that they were going to surpass anything ever known in the hereditary lines behind them. For form, sturdiness, rapidity of growth, bearing power, foliage, and general characteristics they were astonishing. Here was something to be accounted for!

Well, I accounted for it, and later experiments I made, and many made by eminent laboratory scientists along the same general line afterward, confirmed my findings. The facts were, first, that the enforced rest given the plants, as a result of being uprooted, carefully packed, and moved halfway around the globe, had enabled them to store up unusual strength, and second, that the change of climate had so benefited the seedlings that they improved as a child might that had been sent to California for its health. The plums caught right on and became Californiacs in a few weeks; you couldn't find anywhere a better advertisement for rest and a change of climate, not even in the Chamber of Commerce booklets!

Here, then, is one of the processes by which variations in plants are started and, by repetition, repetition, repetition, become fixed in those plants until they separate them, in habits, powers, and characteristics, so widely from their parents and brother and sister plants that they are practically a different species. It is the process of giving the individual plant a new and more favorable environment. For not only does this frequently suit the plant better and enable it to carry its ordinary, known powers, to a higher level, but it brings to light and expresses in the individual latent or dormant hereditary possibilities that otherwise would have remained submerged and, in the end, entirely lost. It is an example of the law of 'use and disuse': the home environment does not call forth this latent characteristic, such as the big and rapid growth of the plum seedlings, but the new environment does and the characteristic springs up from the tiny germ tendency and use strengthens it and repetition, repetition, repetition, fixes it in the plant, and it increases in power generation after generation because it is used and called on and put to work, and is not lying dormant, and threatening, as it probably would in the end, to die out in the heredity from disuse.

Those twelve plum seedlings from Japan were the foundation stones on which I built my plum experiments; two of them came out so well and were so great an improvement, not only on our home plums and on European varieties, but on the Japanese plums that were related to them, that I put them on the market in 1889, four years after they had landed at San Francisco. One of them, described in my year-book as 'very large, conical, heart-shaped, red with white bloom; very good,' was named 'The Burbank' by Professor H. E. Van Deman, Pomologist of the United States Department of Agriculture. The second was a plum with red flesh, very juicy, firm, delicious in flavor and delightful in aroma: it was the very fruit, greatly improved in its new environment, and having developed in it all the possibilities latent in its ancestry, so long dormant there in Japan, which my sailorman had described in the book I had read almost ten years before. It was a dream come true, and in honor of the province whence it was derived I called it 'The Satsuma.'

X

THE introduction of the improved Japanese plums, Satsuma and Burbank, related in the last chapter, was not the result of a plant-breeding experiment, strictly speaking; it was more the result of a college course which I gave those Japanese seedlings, taking advantage of the improvement they themselves showed as the result of the new climate and the rest I have mentioned, and after that a training toward my standards for them, which they took on eagerly and easily, and which made of them far better, far different, and far more valuable fruit trees than when they entered my school.

Meantime I had been accumulating more plum stocks and experimenting extensively with them. The ten left from my Japanese importation proved valuable as a basis for work; by selection for qualities that seemed to me desirable I got plums that were better than anything that had gone before them; after that I went at the work in blossom-time and began cross-breeding.

If the reader is sufficiently interested to read the next few paragraphs he will open for himself, perhaps for the first time, a door to one of the most absorbing studies in all nature; if he is not he can safely skip to later pages. But I promise him that this little excursion into botany will repay him with a greater appreciation of plant life, a new curiosity about flowers that grow everywhere about him, and a higher respect for and understanding of the marvelous workings of Nature. I won't be looking over his shoulder — so he can skip and say he didn't, with perfect impunity!

If you have not studied the subject, do you not wonder how plants perfect the egg that is within the seed, and make it the storehouse for the life that is to come in a succeeding generation? Well, that is what I want to tell you about. For convenience we call the process breeding, and in many ways it is amazingly like the same process in animals. But the plant is fixed in one place, its reproducing organs are the hairlike or wirelike filaments that are to be found in the heart of every blossom, and largely their breeding must be accomplished with the assistance of outsiders. In later papers I propose to mention some of the miraculous and incredible means Nature has for bringing about this essential result in her scheme of things; now I am only going to explain, briefly and simply, the fundamentals of the process.

Every blossom has a number of pollen-bearing filaments that we call *stamens* and one we call the *pistil*. In the *anther* at the end of each *stamen* are produced the pollen grains, each containing a fertilizing sperm, or male life-germ. At the base of the pistil, on the other hand, in the *ovulary*, rest the *ovules*, or eggs. The pollen grains, often so minute that it takes a fine microscope to see them, burst from the anthers in due time, and by chance, by action of wind or insect, or by way of the bills of birds, some of them are transferred to the sticky stigma on the end of the pistil. From that stigma the sperms work through a thin tissue and start throwing out a tube for themselves that eventually finds its way into the ovule, and there the sperms unite with the female life-germ awaiting them in this egg, and fertilization is complete and the beginning of a seed accomplished.

Fertilization is the whole process of uniting the sperm with the egg; in Nature the process may be completed in one individual flower or the pollen may be carried from the anthers of one flower to the stigma of another. Bees have a strange habit of sticking pretty closely to one variety, so that they are perhaps the most useful members of insect society in crossing flowers in the same family, which accounts largely for diversified colors, in the poppies, for example. But other insects are not so particular, and they will go from a honeysuckle to a pansy, from a rose to a fruit blossom — incidentally doing a lot of work that is lost because they carry pollen where it isn't wanted and can't accomplish results.

When man takes a hand he knows what he is about — or he thinks that he does! — and he employs cross-fertilization or, better, cross-pollination, removing the pollen cells from the anther of one flower and carefully placing them on the stigma of another, perhaps of the same variety, perhaps of a different variety and even, as I have done often, of a different species. The insects do some cross-pollination, but it is at random, and only when the heredities of the two plants thus crossed run nearly enough parallel does the cross-pollination bring about actual fertilization and, from it, growable seed.

There are many exceptions to the general rules I

have mentioned and an almost infinite number of possibilities and factors I have not touched on here. For instance, I have not entered on any discussion of the number of flowers, as for instance the rose, that are completely or almost completely sterile and lack either the pistil or the stamens. They have lost the necessity to bear seed because they have been raised from cuttings, or by some such sub-natural method for so long — and therefore they have lost the necessary seed-making and seed-fertilizing machinery. I could go on through a number of volumes on this theme, but I should certainly lose all my audience then; so let me hurry along and pick up the folks who left the train back there when we began our botany class, and proceed with the plum story!

As I said above, the time came when I was ready to begin my attack on the fixed natures of the plums through working with their blossoms, and I took my forceps and glass pollen trays and went into the grounds when the air was heavy with the rich odors and the trees flaming with the beauty of their spring flowers. I began to cross-pollinate.

I do not know anything in the work of the plant developer that offers him more pleasure and satisfaction than this process. Fellow to the bee, the hummingbird, the ant, and the butterfly, he goes from blossom to blossom, not attracted, as they are, by the flamboyant colors with which the trees advertise their wares, but by the rich possibilities inherent in the work; guided not by fragrances, as they are, but by his own records of the characteristics of the fruit, noted the previous year. In my pocket I carry a packet of sheets, on which are noted the working name of the individual fruit, its size, shape, bearing quality, flavor, color, size of pit, texture of flesh, and so on; on each tree I have a marker that identifies the individual and refers me to its record. Like a painter choosing the colors for his palette, I choose the qualities that I desire to combine in the fruit.

Here, the record shows, is a thin, spindling, unpromising tree that bears a firm, luscious, beautiful plum; beyond a sturdy and well-formed tree that gives a sour, unlovely, or small fruit. The pollen from the one goes on to the sensitive, sticky stigma of the pistil of the other, after this second one has been thoroughly cleaned of its own pollen. Next I come to a plum of gorgeous dress that has no aroma or flavor; I know a tree that bears a rich and juicy plum that is drab and unattractive. The two are united in this field marriage ceremony of mine. This seedling offered me, last fall, a firm, well-textured fruit that would be admirable for very late harvesting, if I could only make it *ripen* late. That one yonder is late, but has no other particularly valuable quality. A nice problem, here, very often, because the earlier fruit blossoms earlier, the late one sometimes almost too late for my marriage to be made possible. What do I do then? Well, I find one of the last blossoms possible to the early tree; I hurry to the late one and, to my delight, I find one ambitious little bud rubbing its eyes and waking up to see what sort of a world it is coming into. The poky, late blossom, and the ambitious little early one are my field. And some people think that plant breeding must be tedious and drab sort of work!

The crossing is finished, spring passes, the fruit begins to form, sun, wind, air, and earth do their appointed work, and the fruit slowly takes on color and final form. I watch as eagerly as a child going every morning to see whether or not the cocoon he has found and put in a box filled with leaves has been opened by the butterfly. Is the tree going to bear well? Are the fruits well distributed on the limbs? Does the green fruit hang well, resisting wind and the shaking of the tree? What resistance does it offer pests and disease? These are only a few of the questions I must ask, and that the fruit must answer favorably, or it is doomed. Then the day comes when the first few fruits are ripe. There is a big minute for the plant developer, as well as for the man! Perhaps he has something that will add to the wealth of the orchards of the world — something that will present to mankind a new flavor, aroma, color of flesh, quality, succulence, and delicious taste, or perhaps a step has been made toward one or all of these desirable ends. The first fruit is picked; it is tasted. What is the verdict?

But this is not all. As I have said once before in these papers the mere appearance, taste, texture, sweetness, smell, and flavor of the fruit do not form a complete criterion of its value. Will it ripen without falling from the tree untimely? Will it pick well? Will it keep? Will it cook up? Will it make good jelly? And, even if it cooks well in the kitchen, will it satisfy canners? Or, to put it more fairly, has it special characteristics that make it a possible canning fruit, because in fruit that the big canners will take, the growers of the world have a steady and strong and usually dependable market. On the other hand, if it is not for canners, is it a shipping fruit or one primarily desirable for the home garden or orchard?

Test after test, trial after trial, experiment after experiment — acceptance, approval, partial satisfaction, a question, rejection — the fruit stands or falls according to its ability to measure up, not to one standard or two, but to a dozen, fifty, a hundred! And it must not be assumed that all this is accomplished in one year or two. I have worked for twelve years now on a nectarine that I am hoping this year will prove itself worthy of release to the growers of home orchards. I suppose that nectarine has cost me six thousand dollars in time and in actual expenses — if I get six thousand dollars out of it I will be luckier than I have been with many of my varieties and new creations! As I have said before, we plant inventors cannot patent a new plum, though the man who makes an automobile horn, not far different from the ram's horn with which Joshua blew down Jericho, can get a patent and retire to Southern California and wear silk underclothes the rest of his life!

In speaking of the costs of my experiments I must refer to the enormous number of plants, branches, grafts, and trees that prove utterly valueless, or of a value that seems doubtful to me, considering the high standards I set, and that must be destroyed. My method of speeding up Nature's processes costs me hard work and untiring study and thought; the wholesaling of my experiments — the second half of my method — costs me hard cash. Because Nature requires compensation in all life; what one gains in time or field for experiment in the plant world he must pay for in some other coin. I put my mind to cross-pollination, and plan the work with infinite patience, care and research, where the insects and birds and animals are used while they were about their own businesses, and their efforts are undirected, random, and wasteful. Secondly, I want the largest possible number of variations to choose from, and Nature's laws make it possible for me to get them. But the penalty I pay is the expense of growing the tens of thousands that do not measure up, in order to have the material from which to select the twenty or five or one plant or tree that is what I want or, more likely, leans that way a little farther than its brothers.

Well, from perhaps twenty-five thousand separate and distinct experiments with plums I got at least thirty or forty that had merit and about a score that were a real gift to man. Of these a dozen are now to be found widely used in the orchards and home gardens of this country and some foreign countries; a few have not yet come into their own, and one or two may never be generally enough approved to be well known. This is because tastes and demands differ widely; I do not hesitate to say that every single one of my approved plums is meritorious and a valuable addition to the list of accepted varieties, but I am much in the position of a silk manufacturer who, from thousands of designs offered him, chooses twenty to manufacture into dress goods. He may be a man of taste, discernment, and experience, but it is morally certain that he will be outguessed in certain directions by the women and the dressmakers, and that one or two of the designs he got out, at so much expense, good though they may be by any proper standard of taste or judgment, will be left on his hands at the end of the season, or bought sparingly and finally marked down with a red tag and sold for what they will bring. I have never had the experience of having to hold a remnant sale, myself, or to cut prices to get trade, but I have a few of my creations that are still unrecognized, and perhaps always will be. I smile at this thought, for I am like a mother with ten children: nine of them may become bank presidents and college professors and noted surgeons, or marry such, but something in human nature will make her prefer the runt of the brood and she will die believing that he was, after all, the prize child, and just somehow missed having the chance the others did, or the luck! I'm that way! Probably all of us are!!

Once a new variety is ready for distribution, I am confronted with the necessity of making all this work and planning, and this final achievement, of practical use to myself and the world, and there are three methods by which this is done. I have referred to the plan of filling an order, as in the Empson pea. Not long ago I delivered a very important order to a silk grower in Japan. It was a mulberry tree that, with about the same growing conditions and fertilization as the older varieties, would produce nearly twice as much foliage for the feeding of silkworms. When I had completed the long and complex experiments that ended in success, I forwarded the grafts to Japan, and thus the order was fulfilled.

The second method is to sell a new variety outright to a nurseryman or seedsman. By this method I am completely out of the transaction and the buyer can distribute as he thinks best. Very few of the varieties I have sold in this fashion have been given a name suggestive of me and my work, though most of the buyers, naturally, used my name in the beginning, as a help (which I am proud to say it was) in introducing the novelty. In time, though, the connection had been lost sight of, and that is why I cannot, without looking into my records pretty exhaustively, say just how many new creations and improved varieties, now in general use and in high favor in the orchards and gardens of the world, came first from my experiment farms.

The third method was one I should have preferred, if it had not been made impossible by the work involved and the time required. That is the method of selling direct to the final buyer — the home gardener, the orchardist, or the plant-lover; and the reason I should have preferred it above all others, and the reason I have, as far as I could, pursued it, is that it brought me into immediate and direct contact with the people I have found uniformly the highest type in the world, the people who grow things and take a pride in them and want the best of them, and understand the work involved in producing them. Such as these have made my best friends and my most interesting correspondents; it was impossible for me to indulge my desires to deal with them personally to any great extent, because the work of plant breeding and experimentation has always been too exacting. But I confess that I have sometimes played hookey from the work to put up a fifty cent order from some isolated farm in Nebraska, from some garden lover in New York, or from some enthusiastic and flowery correspondent in Brazil or China or New Zealand, so excited about plants and trees and flowers that he was fairly unintelligible — and in Chinese or Spanish, at that!

Do you wonder that I urge young people to give consideration to the possibilities that lie before them to-day in this field I chose so long ago? And, with my experiences, and with the demonstrations Nature has enabled me to make in the selection and breeding of plants, will you forgive me if I expand the subject a little and comment here, as restrainedly as is possible to one of my temperament, on the appalling folly, waste, and disaster that result on our almost utter ignoring of these same laws when it comes to the rearing of the children of the human race?

We breed animals and plants with ever-increasing care, jealous of their heredities, thoughtful of their environments, cultivating them, preventing bad crosses, eliminating the unfit, and, under Nature's incomparable ordinances, slowly but steadily working toward the millennium of beauty, utility, strength, and productivity that we can see in the far distance for them all. And yet the most precious and the most important children on the planet we breed by chance, from parents thrown together by a process as haphazard as a badly conducted lottery, with dubious backgrounds, into wretched and unfit environments, and we raise them blunderingly, with little thought or care as to their susceptibility on the

one hand and the powerful influences of their surroundings on the other, and then we wonder —
when we stop, occasionally, frightened by some outbreak of war or crime or disease, to give it thought
— what is to be done about the race?

Do you think that those laws which Nature made
and which operate to the improvement of the dog,
the horse, the pig, the hen, the pansy, the dahlia, the
plum, are laws special to the vegetable world and the
world of so-called dumb beasts? Do you think that,
in the perpetuation and betterment of your own
species, you can throw all those laws overboard and
follow none?

No, indeed! Nature is not mocked. Her laws
are as changeless as the universe which they rule;
her judgments are as impersonal and impartial as
they are just, clear, exact, and incredible. What
she requires of us is simple, reasonable, and right-
eous: that enlightened love, as it must rule our
states, dominate our international relations, and fit
us for brotherhood with all mankind, must be the
governing rule in human mating and the underlying
principle in the training of the children that spring
from those matings. And, it is only enlightened and
unselfish love that will lead us to marriages that are
not only holy and happy, but that conform to the
laws of Nature and make beneficent natural selection operative.

Ignorance, bigotry, pride, superstition, and care-
lessness have all conspired to close the door on this
subject for centuries; science is beginning to press it
a little open, and through it there is coming now
such a blazing light as may some day flash over the

whole planet and wither wrong and foolhardiness, and cleanse our minds, and write, in its effulgence and whiteness, a new record for future generations to read.

XI

Soon or late every one comes to a place in this road of life where there is a fork at which he will pause, if he is prudent and thoughtful, and consider which branch to follow. There are plenty of people who come to these diverging paths either without perceiving them or else without being struck by their possible importance; such people follow their noses, as we say, and the way they take becomes a matter of chance only, that may or may not lead to a goal worth seeking. The man who chooses his road, though, has this manifest advantage over the other — that the very act of pondering his course adds to his own powers and, even if his choice be a mistaken one, he is by that much better fitted to pursue it.

As a youth I had several occupations open to me, but I do not think I chose between them with any great difficulty because there was inherent in me so strong a pull toward the study of plant life as a vocation that it was almost inevitable that opportunities in the professions, as an inventor, as an artist or as a teacher — all of which I had open — would be passed by almost without consideration. The fork in my road came when I found myself making money.

Some fifteen years in California firmly established me as a nurseryman and brought me a generous and profitable business. Generally speaking, there is not a great fortune in raising and selling young trees, since the turnover is slow, the market variable, and tastes and fashions in trees undependable. But the very principle on which, from the first, I had based my operations began in time to result in large sales and generous profits — the principle of performing all my experiments and doing all my growing of seedlings and grafts and cuttings on a very large wholesale scale. My name, too, which I guarded jealously from the beginning, was a great asset to me, with a high cash value; in addition to the ordinary nursery business I had many sales of new varieties and novelties that considerably augmented my income.

It was quite apparent, in the early nineties, that I could amass a comfortable fortune as a developer of new trees and flowers and a salesman of nursery stock; the time was not far in the future, I could see, when I could be assured a generous competence, with all that money may bring to one. But I had two certain penalties looming ahead if I were to yield to this temptation to become rich.

The first was that the nursery exacted from me time and energy in the mere business of advertising and selling my wares that I was impatient to give it; the second was that money itself and the fine things it could buy would certainly turn my mind eventually from the hard work involved. The easy course would have been to follow the current of my swelling success, with a vague possibility that, when I was well-to-do, I could afford to experiment with plants without thought as to the expense of the work. But I was a long sight more interested in plant development than I was in money-making, and also I knew quite well that Nature is an exacting mistress and a jealous teacher; she does not reveal herself wholly

to the amateur or the dabbler, and she will not co-
operate fully and generously with the man who
takes her lessons or her work lightly.

Sharp experiences emphasized this truth for me.
I found my experiments interfered with by the demands of my business; two or three important experiments failed signally because I brought to them
a diverted mind; people began to expect more of me,
as a man of business, than they would have pre-
sumed to demand of a plant experimenter devoting
himself to his researches. The temptation to make
money, as I have said, was not an alluring one to me,
but it did require some courage and firmness to cut
myself off from my source of income and devote myself to plant breeding.

That I exerted that firmness with myself and had
that courage was, of course, the determining factor
in my life; as a nurseryman I would have succeeded
in amassing some money and some local fame; as a
plant developer and experimenter, unfettered by
considerations of money-making and unhindered by
the demands a business necessarily would have made,
I was freed. And, a free man, almost careless of
wealth, power, and fame, I was enabled to become a
contributor to the happiness and knowledge and
richness of this earth to all mankind, for all time to
come, and at the same time found, without seeking
either, that money and power and fame all came to
me, in measures undreamed of and unsought. From
this gratifying experience it seems to me safe to
draw one conclusion, namely, that undivided loyalty
to a worthy ideal is richer in its rewards than any
selfish pursuit; the examples of the truth of this

observation are to be found so unfailingly in life that they ought to lead us all to consider whether or not we might be influenced by them when we come to the fork in the road and have our own momentous decision to make.

I need not have gone far for innumerable lessons in my own chosen school to point me to this same conclusion, and perhaps I was influenced unconsciously by those lessons in making my decisior For Nature tells us one thing, over and over again, and in every department of natural history emphasizes it so that, to the naturalist, it begins to be recognized as the one infallible and clear law of existence. It is that the individual is of no importance, while the race is of the first and highest and greatest importance.

Looking back through history I discover that the law operates in human affairs precisely as it does in plant or animal life. It is true that the fittest survive; certain philosophers have from this drawn the conclusion that fitness should be striven for if we are to be happy. It seems to me this is sound reasoning as far as it helps us care for our bodies and improve our minds, but when fitness is taken to mean hardness and hardness is taken to mean selfish ruthlessness, Nature upsets the whole apple-cart of thinkers like Nietzsche by declaring that men are not important but that the race is supreme. Compare Lincoln and Napoleon: the one who thought mainly of and for others and sacrificed himself to make an ideal into a fact, and the other who dreamed of himself as ruling the world and who ceased to be useful to France when he began to think that he was France.

In the field or garden, in the wilderness or on the plain, Nature is teaching us this lesson of humility and service in the individual in a thousand ways — she puts the fact there and if we won't look at it or understand it or apply it, that is our problem and we will be the sufferers. Man alone of all Nature's children thinks of himself as the center about which his world, little or large, revolves, but if he persists in this hallucination he is certain to receive a shock that will waken him or else he will come to grief in the end.

I do not know of any single precept that I have learned from Nature that has been of more importance to me in my life and work, nor of one that I believe is of more value to others. I was some time acquiring it myself, in spite of the fact that it was so clearly before me all the while. As a young man I probably thought Burbank was pretty necessary to the scheme of things, but as the years went on I was shown that it was only what Burbank did for the good of the world that would live and be set down to his credit. I climbed down off the perch pretty quickly when I found I was exaggerating. A pedestal is an uncomfortable location, anyway; if you will look over the wise and the great and the useful you will find them down close to the ground.

In Nature you can find amazingly interesting statements of this law that it is the whole group and not the individual that is important. The most striking examples are those in which the individual is actually penalized for his devotion to his kind or where death follows the reproductive act or such a defensive measure as in the case of the stinging bee.

There are two or three insects I know of that must die when their progeny are insured life; certain shell-fishes are killed when their young or their fellows build on them to keep the colony going; all annual plants give up their life to the life-germ in their seeds, and these are only a few of the instances where self-sacrifice is obligatory and not optional.

But, from these clear lessons to those that we have to find by careful search and study, the law is universal. The mother's instinct to sacrifice herself for her child is based on this law; the great strength and vitality that goes from a plant into its seed and into the mechanism for distributing this seed and insuring it at least a fair chance to find fertile soil is a less obvious instance, but the same ordinance and plan of Nature is behind it.

I believe there is no more interesting study in all life than this of the means and devices by which plants grow, protect and disseminate their seeds, and hardly any one could resist the lure of the subject if he would take the pains to examine a few seed envelopes and watch for himself the process by which they are developed and then utilized to sow the precious seed within. Most of us are perfectly familiar with the envelopes that are provided with burrs or claws or 'stickers' arranged to help the seed attach itself to a passing animal or to the feathers of a bird and cling there until carried to some distant point. Then there are the 'bearded' seeds, such as those of the barley or what children call the 'foxtail,' which have containers barbed so that they will actually dig themselves into the loose leaf-mould or top-soil of their abiding place and hang on there quite tenaciously until the winter rains come and the seed germinates and takes root.

Another variety of seeds and envelopes is covered with a coating of a sticky substance that adheres to that which it touches; another the envelopes that 'explode' and shoot their seeds in every direction, sometimes so violently as to endanger an eye. Examine the red clover or oxalis plant when its pods are ripening. You will find them green in appearance and not, like beans or peas, changing color and drying up. The heat of the sun will draw and draw on the moisture content of these red clover envelopes and suddenly the fastenings of the long pods will give and the hard little white seeds will fly out, with such force that you can feel them hit cheek or hand. The process in the bean or pea is the same — the drying-up of the pod — though it goes farther before the explosion occurs, with a twisting motion that actually gives some of the seeds the curve of a baseball pitcher.

Still other seeds, and in some cases, the envelopes, or 'fruits' themselves, are winged, so that they will fly a considerable distance, borne by the breeze or even floating as they fall and scattering quite a way. The gladiolus and the coreopsis are just two of the great number of winged seeds, while the maple, the ash, and the elm tree have winged fruits.

Closely akin to the winged seeds are those made to float on water — and many between the two will both float and fly. A sort that will interest children is the 'pepper-pot' variety of envelopes, like those of the snapdragon, the poppy, or the tobacco plant. These have openings sometimes so nearly like a pepper-pot or salt-shaker that they would make excellent designs for silversmiths to follow: there are enough seeds in each pod of the tobacco plant to keep a family in smoking materials if they would all grow, and incidentally, if you can get hold of a microscope you would be amazed at the beauty of each seed, so tiny that it is like a grain of sand, and yet each a perfect little gem of beauty — bronze, flecked with gold, and shaped something like a brazil nut. This employment of a small microscope, by the way, will add something to your life that you would not take a good deal for, if you tried it. You set considerable store by the movies, but a microscope will open to you a world of beauty and interest the motion picture camera cannot reach — and right in your own garden, or the nearest park, or even in a window-box or a flower pot, if that is the best you are able to do, where you are.

Another kind of seed-container and another kind of seed is the tough variety, made so that it would take a burglar to get into it, and of such material that even the powerful juices of the stomach of an animal cannot disintegrate it. Plenty of seeds are eaten by animals and pass through their bodies without the slightest change; if the animal has wandered a few miles during the day you can understand that the free ride the seed had, without the expense of a ticket and with a comfortable berth all made up for it, will land it somewhere where it can have a new chance to take root and perhaps a better chance than the parent plant had.

This, incidentally, is an interesting study in itself — the reason for the arrangement Nature makes for distributing seed as widely as possible. There is, of course, the need for avoiding competition with its fellow seeds of the same variety, and the big showy plants that take lots of room will be found, usually, to have devices for disseminating seed widely, whereas as a rule plants that can stand up in a crowded community, such as the California poppy and the johnny-jump-up, are content to let their seeds fall in close.

In a broader and more important sense there is an excellent reason for this broadcasting of seed and especially for the devices by which it is carried long distances, perhaps by animals or birds or perhaps by floods and high winds: that is, the long experience some plants have had with the vicissitudes of existence and the constant, though slow, change that is going on all over the world in character of soil, climate, temperature, moisture conditions, and the like. Many species have found their old homes rendered unlivable for them; they would have been wiped out (as I suppose a good many thousands or tens of thousands have been, probably) by some cataclysmic or epochal change; but if a few seeds, even, had reached distant areas or distant lands or other continents by this dispersion I am speaking of and found root there, the species was preserved, to assume the great task Nature commits to us of carrying life on.

It all comes back, you see, to the importance of the race. The individual is important to himself, and you will find innumerable interesting examples, some of which I have discussed already in these papers, by which individual plants are enabled to see themselves through a hard winter, or drought, or unfavorable conditions, or even visitations of plant sicknesses, but you will be forced in the end to the conclusion that it is for the sake of re-creating itself in seed that the plant lives and struggles, and often sacrifices itself — that the species or the race is the main consideration, and that the individual is, to Nature, a mere pawn in the Great Game — a mere thread or bit of color in her Immortal Pattern.

Perhaps a naturalist, with seventy years of work and observation behind him, can be forgiven if he preaches a little, and it seems to me this is a good time to preach briefly on the theme of Service. That is a vastly overworked term, in our modern times, and is made to apply to salesmanship and slumming and about everything in between, but it is still a good word and a good idea to contemplate. I will bet a straw hat to a felt one that, if you are tired of your job and discouraged with life and down in the mouth about the way you are treated, you have got a little mixed about your importance to the scheme of things, but I will bet an entire new suit of clothes against a poor necktie that, if you are happy, capable, liked, and trusted, you are giving the world or your family or your employers or your employees a little more than is expected or than you are paid for or than you get back. I never knew a naturalist, or a Nature-lover, who was a pessimist, though I'll confess I have known quite a number of writers and professors and near-scientists who were; I think that you have only to live with Nature for a while and keep your eyes and ears and hearts and minds open to become impressed with the hopefulness and beauty and fairness of the scheme — to become, in other words, an optimist. There is nothing mysterious nor complicated about getting the right adjustment to your environment: if you can realize that you are important to the scheme only in so far as you contribute something to it, why, mercy on us, you will find a smile coming easy, a laugh second nature, and a cheerful, helpful word right at the tip of your tongue from morning till night.

I know it is unfashionable to preach the doctrine of happiness and the value of unselfishness, and that I take tremendous risks of being set down as very ordinary. Well, I never thought much of the fashions, anyway, and as for being ordinary, it runs in the family, and is the thing about the Burbanks and the Rosses and the Edisons and Jordans and Lindseys and Muirs and Burroughses and such tribes that I take the most joy in and feel the greatest pride about. So you will get small comfort from reading me out of the Blue Book on that score!

Just a little while back I had a letter, typical of many received during my lifetime, from a man who had read something I had said in print about gardening on a small lot, and who wrote that he had gone out and bought a hoe and a fork and some seeds and was now raising all his own vegetables and was beginning to branch out with flowers. That letter did me as much good as a tonic, because it showed me, for perhaps the one millionth time, that an enthusiast for Nature can wield a considerable influence in getting other folks to turn that way too. I do not think these papers will add greatly to the

sum of human knowledge, since I am setting down
in them very little that is new or heretofore unheard
of; what I do hope is that they will awaken the interest of readers in Nature and her processes, not
only for the fascination and delight of the theme
but because of the lessons that the study must bring
to your attention and the influence some of those
lessons may have on the lives of my fellows and particularly of their children.

And so I keep yielding to the temptation to tell
you more of the miracles and marvels of Nature,
as I have discovered or encountered them. And it
seems to me important to say that what I am setting
down here has come to me mostly through my own
observations and experiments or has been deduced
from my own experiences with plant life. I have
read omnivorously and over a very wide field, and I
have learned from the work and reasoning of others,
but I do not believe that there is a single fact or
statement or conclusion in this series of papers that
has not impressed itself on my mind either through
actual contact or deliberation or else through practical demonstration of statements made by others
and tested by myself. From the beginning of my
work I was never skeptical, but I had to prove
things. My lifelong adherence to the scientific principles enunciated by Charles Darwin was not the result of any hasty acceptance of his soundness; in fact
some of his theories I seriously doubted, from my
own slight experience. But as time went on I had
greater and greater opportunities of putting his
theories to the test of garden bed and field row, and
the older I have grown the more firmly have I been

convinced that he was the master and that all the others are mere pupils, like myself.

A young man once wrote me asking which book he should read by Mendel, the great scientist who concerned himself with the problem of heredity and hereditary laws, to inform himself of the scientific facts in that field. I wrote him in reply something like this: 'My advice to you is to start Mendel by reading Darwin, and then let Mendel go and read more Darwin.' And in one of my books I used a somewhat similar sentence: 'Read Darwin first, then read the modern Mendelists, and then — go back to Darwin!' I did this because I found many qualified scientists stating conclusions which I could not demonstrate nor use as a working basis, but found Darwin always measuring up to the tests and the facts and never fumbling nor going astray through a too-close application to a favorite theory or a fixed notion. I had no fixed notions except the single notion that Nature was the final authority and that the interpretations put upon her laws and practices and idiosyncrasies and apparent contradictions by scholars, scientists and philosophers were only suggestive and seldom conclusive. Darwin appeals to me as an exception, but he used reason and logic and common sense in addition to research, experimentation and analysis, and if he had to choose between a clear probability on the one hand and a closed door or a negation on the other he would state the clear probability as a safe assumption, and scientific enough to suit him.

We give a good deal of attention to the wonder of the growth of the mind of a child, but it seems to

me that the wonder does not cease with childhood. My own mind, I know, has grown day by day;
I have seen myself lose intolerance, narrowness,
bigotry, complacence, pride, and a whole bushel-
basket of other intellectual vices through my contact with Nature and with men. And when you take
weeds out of a garden it gives you room to grow
flowers. So, every time I lost a little self-satisfac-
tion or arrogance, I could plant some broadness or
love of my kind in the place, and after a while the
garden of my mind began to bloom and be fragrant
and I found myself better equipped for my work
and more useful to myself and others as a consequence.

The raw materials to make this growth possible,
though, do not come from introspection or selfishness. They come from the application of lessons
from without — the influence of environment, repeating itself over and over again on the sensitive
plate of the brain and being transformed there, as
sunshine and foods are transformed in the leaf of the
plant, into material for the beautifying of the mind
and the enriching of the soul. You have it in your
power only to keep the brain sensitive to impressions
and the heart and mind and soul adaptable to
growth; you have 'the power to vary,' and the extent to which you utilize and benefit from that
power depends on you and on no one else.

XII

SUPPOSE we get back on the main track, now, after having taken a stop-over while I aired my views, and consider some more of the miracles and marvels of Nature in plant life — miracles and marvels that, after all, have sound reasons underlying them and simple explanations behind them, if we will look carefully enough, and from all of which we can draw lessons that help in our understanding of human problems.

There was considerable made, back in 1908 and 1910, about a stoneless plum I was working on. Horticulturists and scientists said it was impossible; newspapermen, looking around for something novel and interesting to write about, made up stories about it as another proof that I was a 'wizard of plant life.' I tried for a while to deny the wizardry part of the narrative, but no newspaperman wants a good story spoiled, and the magic of the stoneless plum received a lot more attention than the homely truth.

The fact is that the stoneless plum came from a cutting sent me by one of my volunteer collectors in France: he had taken it from a very old tree and he was not able to account for the fact that the fruit had no stone, or none to speak of. He merely sent it along for what it was worth. I don't suppose there was another such tree in existence, and it would be difficult to account exactly for it. It may have been a variation — a mutation — caught by some old chap who was curious about it, and grafted into one of his plum trees, or it may have been a seedling that had forgotten to provide material for its stone and had developed into a freak of Nature.

I seized on it at once, as having possibilities for the development of a new, stoneless variety of plums, and I worked with it for years. It was the beginning of a stoneless plum and a stoneless prune which I have; they are not yet entirely satisfactory, but in time they will become so, if they are intelligently cross-bred with established and valuable varieties and if selection is made that will weed out all the seedlings that show undesirable traits and will preserve and foster those that lean or tend toward desirable ones. It is the process to which I have referred so often — the mingling of heredities to break up uniformity and accustomed habits of growth and fruiting and to cause the appearance of a large number of variations; then the careful selection as between these several variations that will eventuate in time in a clean-cut, fixed variety having the characteristics desired: — in this case, size, flavor, sturdiness of growth, productivity, and fine quality, all coupled with the entirely new characteristic of stonelessness.

So much is simple, but not so simple is the solution of the question: 'Whence came that first stoneless plum on some hillside in France?' One scientific school would call it a mutation — an accidental and sudden variation with no known or traceable cause. Another would maintain that there is no such thing as a sudden mutation, but that the he-

redity of the plant somewhere contained the stoneless quality and that it finally cropped out in this
plum. I am convinced that both are partially right:
my experience leads me to believe that small, gradual, persistent variations occur in plants as they
do in animals and in man, and also I believe that
these slight variations, impressed on the heredity
of the plant, may become submerged and lie for untold generations in the seed without developing until, without any reason I can definitely state, but
under some such environmental influence as soil,
climate, moisture, or the presence of a food value
exactly suited to the demands of that sleeping trait
in the seed, the old, dormant trait springs to life in a
single individual plant, and we are startled to find a
stoneless plum tree!

There are similar occurrences in the human family. What is it causes this young man, soberly bred,
well educated, of a refined and cultivated family,
suddenly to turn thief or murderer or rascal? You
may look back through five or six or eight generations and find no trace of any such tendency as is
manifest in him, yet somewhere along the line, perhaps farther back than you can go, with your in-
complete records, you will find a strain of crimi-
nality or a tendency toward a moral outbreak.
Given that taint, no matter how remote, you have
only to put the mother of the unborn child, or the
infant himself, into an environment that gives the
old, sinister trait encouragement, or you have only
to put on the boy some pressure, mental or physical,
such as worry, or over-indulgence, or a bad illness,
and abruptly the weakness comes to the surface

and there is a job for the police department or the insane asylum or the penitentiary!

It has taken us a long time to realize that criminal tendencies or mental deficiencies are not often the fruits of lax training or of individual perversions. Society and the law used to sit back complacently until the wayward boy actually stole a ham or the weak-minded woman actually set fire to her house or tore up all her clothing, and then the officers would come along and clap the 'offender' into a jail or an asylum. Now we can see — and Nature herself has taught us the truth! — that the weakling and the perverse and the feeble-minded must be given a proper environment early and their stronger and better talents and traits and tendencies accented and brought out, so that perhaps the bad characteristics will be submerged or drowned out of the unfortunate. Often it is found that the heredity is too strong for the environment — the taint has permeated the whole system, and no care or love or kindness or education will conquer it. I have often been asked what prescription I would give in such a case; I can only answer that, in my gardens, dangerous weeds are uprooted and destroyed, weak plants are removed, and no tainted individual is permitted to bear seed, or even to develop pollen, lest an entire field be affected and the strong, the good, and the beautiful be cursed with the evil influence of one depraved individual. Nature hires no criminal lawyers and issues no writs of habeas corpus for the vicious or weak plant; I never heard of her letting out a mad dog on probation. Perhaps her way with plants and animals is not as good a way as man's with man, but it would require a long session and some eloquent arguments to convince me of the fact!

There is no branch of human life or activity for which you cannot find some analogy in the garden or field, and, if you examine the matter closely enough, none about which you cannot learn a good deal to your advantage from studying Nature's methods, laws, and processes. The subordination of the individual to the race, and Nature's habit with hereditary taints and traits, are no more striking than her strong prejudice, as I believe, in favor of individuality in plant or animal; what seems a paradox, at first view, is really consistent with her whole scheme. Let us examine this interesting fact more closely.

All plants have a strong individuality, sometimes only apparent from close scrutiny, and others that your own dog could see. The individual traits of varieties and species, taken as a whole, are the most noticeable. Consider desert growth, in which I first became interested when I began my work, thirty years ago, with the cactus. The outstanding characteristic of our deserts is lack of moisture. The plant, to persist in the arid wastes, had first to conserve moisture and store every available drop of water it could lay root or leaf on. It became sparse, wiry, and deep-rooted, in the sagebrush and saltweed, for example, or, as in the cactus, it developed big, tough-skinned reservoirs in its leaves. But, having conquered death from drought, it found itself by that very fact exposed to a new danger — the danger of destruction by animals forced, because the desert growth was sparse, to turn for food to the few varieties that had survived the rigors of the climate. So here was a new enemy to defeat, and the desert plants put out their energies in battle and eventually were so dry and bitter and tough that no animal, not even a burro, would get much satisfaction out of them, or else they put out spines to make themselves about as poor an article of diet as you could find anywhere.

That is individuality — variation — in the species, called forth by environment and entering into the heredity of the plant so that it will breed true, finally, as long as its surrounding conditions remain unchanged. But the same power to vary runs through the whole of plant life and down to individuals of the same species: as there are no two men exactly alike so there are no two roses or lilies or redwood trees exactly the same. Partly this individuality inside families of plants is due to differences, often minute, in environment — more shade or less moisture, a variation in the soil, or what not; but mainly it is due to Nature's insistence on variation, because from variation she gets that adaptability in the plant which enables it to resist enemies or make friends and so to preserve life and insure the perpetuation of the species come what may in the way of change of locality, change of climate, visitations of disease or of destructive animals, and so on.

Nature favors this variability, I say; I believe she favors it in man and that, to her, the genius, the creative spirit, the originator, the inventor, the daring thinker, the pioneer and explorer, whether in finding new lands and charting strange seas or in marching ahead in scientific fields and breaking away from orthodox beliefs, are all expressions of her desire for progress. There is no more interesting example of the parallel between Nature's process in plant life and in human life than is to be found in our own America. In this great garden she has cross-pollinized races and tribes and the people of every nation; the result has been a wholesale production of hybrid seedlings presenting every conceivable phase of variation; some of these crosses have turned out badly, and society has selected out the worst of them and discarded them, others that are none too useful are still growing like weeds, but from the whole bed have sprung such new and striking and useful individual plants as Henry Ford, Theodore Roosevelt, Jacob Riis, Joseph Pulitzer, and hundreds more. In fact there are very few Americans whose recent ancestors have not brought to the family some blood of a people other than English — we are crosses within the last few generations from every nation under the sun, and our variations have produced wide differences in capacity and ability, and a very bouquet of geniuses and original thinkers.

Now observe how the apparent paradox of Nature's emphasis of *race* importance and her prejudice in favor of *individual* differences and *individual* superiorities merges into a simple statement of the same law in two forms. The superior individual contributes more to the welfare of the race than the ordinary or the sub-normal individual; each genius or leader or creative artist helps to make his fellows more adaptable and better fitted to carry on the struggle of life; just as in the plant world, variation is necessary to adaptability, and adaptability is essential to the conquest of the changing conditions of the world and to the overcoming of adverse environment or the seizing of the advantages of a favorable environment. Nature seems to be full of exceptions to every rule, but on analysis we find that the underlying law is immutable and the underlying principle changeless and infallible.

Let us go into a swamp or a crowded and neglected garden for another lesson from the plant world that is applicable to our own problems and that may have a moral for us who consider ourselves so superior to the lower orders of life. In the swamp there is a rich accumulation of plant foods, there is heat, there is water. The growth is tangled, dense, luxuriant, and usually partly poisonous. In the neglected garden everything has run riot and weeds and flowers elbow and push and pant and struggle to maintain life — an overcrowded city of inferior individuals, all seeking root-room and breathing space and a place in the sun. How like a crowded city — the swamp like the slums, the neglected garden like the business section or the apartment house district!

In the swamp the tendency is steadily toward rank growth. To be sure, the swamp may produce orchids — the most beautiful and fragile and delicate bloom known. I remember once being asked if I had ever done any work to improve orchids. I stared at the questioner for a moment or two, fumbling for a reply. And then I said, perhaps a little impatiently: 'Improve orchids? But who on earth would dream of wanting them improved?' Well, the orchid is a development of tropical jungle growth. Beautiful! It is the rich, effulgent product of an environment that has in it many elements of disease and destruction. Our slums are like that — breeding crime and disease, overcrowded, producing unfortunates and unfit, and yet occasionally giving us a great musician, a great actress, or a great merchant because the densely populated area has good blood and good heredity here and there in it and because the conditions are exotic and the strong individuals produce strong mentalities, strengthened and enriched by the very force of the pressure about them. Neither the jungle nor the slum is desirable, and some day we will do away with both, as we are gradually doing away with our own swamps in the South; until that time comes we must be content with the occasional orchid of genius who is the fruit of that environment.

The crowding of our cities is like the crowding of a neglected garden, and there is where spindling, weak, attenuated growths occur, and where the average of strength, bodily and mental, is lowered by the struggle and the pressing in of a multitude of weeds. The growth of cities is unhealthy for a nation, but I seem to see a tendency to spread out into suburbs and outlying districts that may solve a problem that has caused disaster in past history. Our task is to go into that neglected garden and, by pruning, weeding, opening up breathing spaces such as parks and playgrounds, and giving the human plant such environmental advantages as education and training, to enable them to meet the competition of the crowd and reach a fuller stature, mentally and physically.

Plants must have elbow-room, and when we give it to them they improve and grow strong. When a man is crowded down to a bare subsistence and pushed upon on all sides by necessity, by competition, by economic demands, he has little chance for growth. He cannot even grow up to the measure of his possibilities; he becomes more and more like all his fellows. There is no chance for variation — that is as clear as daylight — and without variation there is no progress and without progress there soon begins to be retrogression.

Let us turn to another of the laws governing the development of variations and variant types in the plant world that has an important bearing on our knowledge of the training and development of the human plant. I have written a good deal about inducing new characteristics in flowers, fruits, and trees, but I have not yet gone much into the relative difficulties presented by the hereditary strains in those plants. The California poppy, I have said, lent itself to manipulation very readily, and that was because it was in a transitional stage from some earlier form of ancestry and none of its qualities was firmly fixed. On the other hand the cactus was a hard nut to crack.

These two examples will serve well to bring out the point I have in mind. A change in the nature of a plant, as in the nature of a human being, must take into account the length of time the heredity has been unchanged in the particular you are driving at. You can bend a plant toward a change in color, let us say, without much trouble, but you would have considerable difficulty in developing a change in root structure, number of petals, or in leaf form. That is because the color was added after all the other characteristics of the plant — it is a more modern improvement, whereas the whole life history of the plant may have seen very little change in its form and structure. The poppy had no old, fixed, stubborn heredity, therefore it could be led to grow tall or dwarfed, golden or yellow or red, and with large or small blossoms, almost with no effort at all. The cactus, fighting for existence for hundreds or thousands of generations, had its characteristics deeply rooted and with few variations from the normal.

In the cactus I wanted two important improvements — a more luxuriant growth and the elimination of the dangerous spines. The usual desert cactus is covered with pin-cushions full of the sharpest and most active little spines; it is almost impossible to put a finger on the plant without getting scores or hundreds of those tiny stings into your flesh. Once there you cannot brush them out or even pick them out without the greatest difficulty. I had a man working for me about fourteen years ago who got a cactus spine in the end of his finger and who never has succeeded in getting it out, so that there is to this day a tiny discolored spot under his nail where that obstinate cactus spine has settled down for its old age.

Of course this meant that the cactus, which, except for the spines, would make succulent and heavily productive food for cattle, was valueless, and my de-

sire was to take off the spines, develop a great productivity of 'slabs' or leaves, and render our American deserts and semi-arid sections useful to cattlemen. But I had lighted on a habit of the cactus
that was almost as old as the plant itself: one of its
first developments had been this protective armor
against foraging beasts. The work was slow, and
the set-backs numerous. That I succeeded in the
end was due to persistent selection — repetition,
repetition, repetition of the same characteristics in
the chosen plants and the destruction, in enormous
and expensive quantities, of all the rest. It was like
teaching a dog — by telling him the same thing
over and over and over again, always in the same
tone of voice and with the same gestures and word-
ing, until he accommodates himself to a new habit
and responds to your will.

In the end I succeeded in fixing the spineless
quality in my cactus; as long as the plants are grown
from slabs (the leaves) the result will be a cactus
free from spines. But even the spineless variety will
produce variations when grown from the seeds, so
that cactus seedlings cannot be relied on. This is
because the spineless characteristic, or habit, is the
last one added to the cactus, and it will take scores
or hundreds of generations, perhaps, to make the
plant forget all about spines, when it comes to the
instinctive manufacture of its seeds, and come permanently and invariably true.

Here is a marvelous truth for human beings in
their own problems, especially the problems of education. You cannot breed out nor educate out the
oldest traits of men easily, but you can succeed in

almost any given line provided you stick to that
line and persist and are patient and intelligent.
Selfishness and greed and hate are old, old human
characteristics; the love of music and dancing and
drama are newer, relatively speaking. Therefore
when you begin to work with a child you can accomplish wonders in awakening in him an appreciation of music or art or even in inducing in him some
talent along æsthetic lines, but when you start to
eradicate the older traits you find yourself bucking
the heredity of a hundred thousand years, maybe,
and you must not expect to transform a fighting
boy or a liar or a glutton overnight. It will probably take twenty years to make even a faint impress
on him, and if you want to get permanent results
that he will pass on to his children you had better
make up your mind to use up ten or fifteen generations on the job!

We have been attempting to educate the American Indian and Christianize him, to break up Mafia
among Italian immigrants, to stop tong-wars among
the Chinese, and to elevate the whole negro race
from slavery to a high type of citizenship. With
individuals we have made progress — the variations
in those people have been wide enough to give us
certain latitude and make possible certain gains.
But taken as a whole we have not established any
records; we have succeeded in putting a few tong
murderers and black-hand criminals to death, in
filling the negro full of wrong notions, and in getting
the Indian to the place where he will attend Sunday-
School along about Christmas time, just before the
annual barrels of old clothes and worn-out toys come

to the missionaries from Eastern friends or sup-
porters. Every one of those four types has inherent
in it fine possibilities, but we have gone at the job
largely from the wrong end: we have passed laws
and put on policemen to enforce them, but we haven't
taken hold of the more recently acquired hereditary
characteristics of each one and worked back from
those, slowly and patiently, toward the underlying
and motivating heritages and inherited tendencies.

Back of all life is a common law: it is not by studying the child or the seaweed or the rose or the star or
the dog alone that we come to that law, but by
studying all of Nature and learning to harmonize
our facts and erect a balanced structure of truth.
At times we come on contradictions, paradoxes, enig-
mas, and we become discouraged and pessimistic
and baffled. It seems, often, that there is no scheme
of things, but that what we call Nature is only a
blind, fatuous, endless struggle between two forces
— positive and negative, constructive and destructive, the upward pull and the downward drag.
Scientists, thinkers, philosophers all have their dark
moments, and some of them come only to box canyons from which, in the end, they can see no escape
and in which they perish, proclaiming that life is a
meaningless and abortive chaos.

But, if we will catch and hold each single ray of
light that shines through, and if all the rays are
focussed by science and philosophy and education,
the brilliance of the real truth will persist and grow
and spread, until its light will illumine all the dark
pages of the book of life and every line and precept
will be clear to read and simple to understand.

XIII

NATURE is our only reliable and authentic teacher.

If we go back far enough we find that everything we study, learn, and know, and all the facts from which we build our theories and even our dogmas, come from Nature's own book, though many of the lessons and much of the knowledge passes through and is modified or interpreted or adapted by the mind of man. That is why science is at once the most fascinating and the most basic subject we have to ponder, since science teaches us the laws and practices of the natural world, whether of man or animal, of flower or tree, of air or water, of earth or star, of physical property or of mental process.

Except for my very early years my schools have been only the University of Nature. I matriculated in the College of Horticulture, Department of Market Gardening, but I finished that course in a short time and entered the laboratory where Nature teaches Plant Breeding. I can't say that I have graduated from that branch of the institution even yet — there is so much to learn! — but in the years that I have been a student I have spread out considerably and taken something of pretty nearly every course my Alma Mater offers except Football and Public Speaking!

And here is the great difference between my favorite University and the schools men build: the ambitious and interested student can enroll for life

and take every course offered, and each fact he adds
to his store, and each semester of work he does fits
him precisely and definitely for the next subject
ahead, without any loss of motion, and without
learning a line that is superfluous to him, or purely
ornamental, or simply academic!

I have spoken before of the close parallel I find, as
all naturalists and Nature-lovers must find, between
every branch and form and expression of life. By
studying fishes or rabbits or lions or buttercups you
cannot avoid learning about man; if you know something of cell life or crystals you can easily grasp the
elemental facts as regards stars and worlds. A diligent pursuit of the subject of *what we are* lays the
foundation for a study of *why* and *how;* you cannot
delve into the laws of ethnology without grounding
yourself in the fundamentals of sociology, and history becomes to you simple, eloquent and intelligible
when you have mastered the principles of biology.
They are interrelated — they are like a spider's
web, woven of the same materials, laid in a pattern
almost geometrical in its perfection, and every strand
at once supporting or bracing every other and being
supported and braced by the others.

Let me be clearly understood (if I am not thus far)
as regards this great force or influence I write of so
often in these chapters as Nature. I have used the
capital initial for emphasis, and because I have tried
to be interesting and give my story at least one
principal character or heroine, but in doing this I
may have been guilty of leading some of my readers
astray, in my gratitude to Nature, as to my concept
of her powers and principles, and my own belief as

to her dominance of our world as we know it and are a part of it.

In the first place it is only figuratively that I speak of Nature as a personality or an entity. Nature is not personal, any more than her manifestations in law and operation are personal. She is compounded of all those processes which move through the universe to effect the results we know as Life and of all the ordinances which govern that universe and make that Life continuous. She is no more the Hebrews' Jehovah than she is the physicist's Force; she is as much Providence as she is Electricity; she is not The Great Pattern any more than she is Blind Chance; these are but names we give her according to the concept of her we are trying to express. It is impossible for the mind of man to grasp much except what he can realize through his five senses, therefore we have long since contracted the habit of apostrophizing forces and powers and elements we cannot define or analyze: — therefore the impelling influence behind Life as we know it we speak of as Nature.

Natural laws and operations and processes are in fact entirely impersonal. To our little minds some of the things Nature does are cruel, ruthless, wasteful, or even wrong, just as, to our imperfect visions, she appears sometimes beneficent, kindly, sympathetic, and helpful. Yet in both we are mistaken, for Nature takes just as much cognizance of the deadly snake as of the greatest statesman; she gives no more thought to the baby in your arms than she does to the menacing typhoid bacilli on the foot of that fly that is crawling toward the baby's lips; she is jealous of the dainty flower in your garden just as much as, and no more than, she is jealous of the scorpion that hides at its base or the murderous renegade who waits for his prey in the shadow of the garden wall. To her the flea, the cockroach, the hyena, the buzzard, the leopard, the cobra are as important as the dog who loves and guards you, the horse who understands and works for you, the young girl in her lover's embrace, the child at its mother's knee in prayer, or the mature man on whom depend the happiness and well-being of a gracious wife and a family of lovely children.

Our egotism has always tried to squirm out from under this self-evident truth, and we have, from the beginning of conscious thought and the first glimmerings of reason in the human mind, tried to sugarcoat the fact with superstitious legends, stories, tales, and religious parables and teachings. We don't like to admit that we — 'a little lower than the angels' — are no more important to Nature than the mosquito that stings us or the lightning flash that destroys us, and our poets and theologians have invented pleasing fables that give us a sense of superiority and help us to believe that we are the favorites of the universe and immune to the operation of some of the laws.

But down in our hearts we know that this isn't the fact; if we reason about it a little we will see that the only advantage we have is the advantage of being better equipped, through gradual growth and development in past ages, to meet life and to conquer our natural enemies in life. To my way of thinking we cannot too soon rid ourselves of super-

stitions in this respect: I have learned from Nature
that dependence on unnatural beliefs weakens us in
the struggle and shortens our breath for the race,
and that it is only by learning about Nature and her
laws, and by applying our knowledge to the end that
we are better equipped to obey and take advantage
of those laws, that we can actually make ourselves
masters of life and winners in the great battle.

In that last sentence lies the key to the whole
secret. Everything Nature has taught me, in my
seventy years of work in her University, emphasizes
the fact that natural laws are incredibly exact,
marvelously correlated, and infallibly just; that
they afford a working basis for usefulness, happiness,
prosperity, and health, and that if we lack any one
of those four great boons it is because we have
violated some law or neglected to perform some
duty Nature has laid upon us. Consider for a moment what life would be if the laws were made —
as it sometimes seems many man-made laws are! —
for the peculiar benefit and protection of some type
or class or particular person. Suppose the lion
multiplied as codfish do, by the million! Suppose
that cholera germs could be killed by no antiseptic
or chemical provided in the whole pharmacopœia of
Nature! Suppose that tyrants and war-makers were
never gluttons, never consumptive, never subject
to brain fever and physical breakdown! Suppose that
there was one law for the wolf and another for the
dog that keeps him away; one rule for the bullet of a
thief and another for the bullet of the sheriff; one ordinance governing the master and another the serv-
ant — what sort of a world would this be for us all?

The impartial and implacable character of all Nature is what recommends her most strongly to me; once I know what she has to say I can order my life accordingly, take up and pursue my work, face and conquer my difficulties, attack and solve my problems, always confident that the umpire of the game is not going to change the rules on me in the middle of an inning, but will call my opponent out with certain, sure, unfailing, and instant decision, and, on the other hand, will never give me four strikes by mistake or overlook the fact that I failed to touch first base! It is the very impersonality of Nature that impels in me the reverence I have for her and the eagerness I show to know all her laws that I can master and apply them with all the diligence and intelligence I possess.

It is this Law behind life that I speak of as Nature. It expresses itself in a thousand ways, it speaks all languages, it dominates all growth, and it underlies all the facts and operations of inanimate as well as animate things. In an early chapter I referred to the dispute among scientists and scholars as to whether Nature's regulations and processes work for improvement or not; so much depends on the point of view that we will, perhaps, never answer that question to the satisfaction of all. There can be no question that, in certain directions, improvement is noticeable; one side declares it cannot be proved that this improvement is more than relative and points out that it is neither universal nor absolute, while the other asserts that the world is a better place in which to live than ever it was before and that those human beings, animals and plants that have adapted themselves to their environments and have survived are better types all around than their ancient ancestors. As I have said more than once, I am an optimist; to me the improvement in all life seems to be evident, and I cannot help but feel that natural law works toward improvement, if not toward perfection. But here we go a little outside the realm of science and a step into the realm of metaphysics or philosophy or something where, in the last few weeks, I have been told emphatically by some of my brethren of the cloth that I do not belong. So, although I am on their side in this particular dispute, I think I will keep a close mouth and look wise, as the boys say!

Now, having made myself clear as to my belief about Nature and my use of the capital letter in these chapters when I refer to her or her laws or operations, I want to go on again and write something more about the University of Nature where I have studied so long. I think of myself as a scientist, if that describes one who has made himself thoroughly conversant with one of the innumerable phases or branches of the fundamental principles of life, but I should much rather be thought of, as I always think of myself, as a naturalist. A true naturalist must be scientific, but it does not at all follow that a scientist is either a lover or a student of nature. All those sciences that deal with organs, functions, classifications, measurements, indexes, names, details, formulas, analysis and minutiæ may be carried on in a world of dead things; the naturalist deals with the living and, largely, deals with it in terms of life. He is a humanist; he wants to find out what relation there is between his branch of nature and his fellowman; his primary interest is in the application of the laws he reads; his object is to interpret Nature to man. Emerson was a naturalist, Thoreau and Agassiz and Dana were naturalists, Hudson and Fabre and Beebe are naturalists; there is a long list of them, and they have helped to breathe the breath of life and interest and meaning into the dry bodies of the sciences. They, like Lamarck and Darwin, went to the fountain head of all knowledge for their conceptions of life, and that is what I have always wanted to do and that is what I have done through my seventy-year course in Nature's great school.

As a very young man I saw the fundamental laws behind all life and development — the laws I have discussed in previous chapters. I had in me a mixed heredity of inclinations and abilities that made me versatile: I could draw a little, paint a little, sing a little, invent a little, turn my hand to almost any of the mechanical or manual arts, and do a day's work I was not ashamed of at carpentering, lathing, shingling, brick-making, teaming, operating machinery of almost any kind, or could do steam-fitting and plumbing, glazing and house-painting, or running a forge or a lathe, with some facility. Any one of these inborn capacities might well have been developed into something to give me a life-work; it was not until I had been some time in Nature's University that I discovered I could go pretty nearly as far as I liked with all of them because I had added theoretical knowledge to practical bent.

Let me illustrate what I mean. I had studied medicine for a part of two years, in my early twenties, but had given up the idea of following the profession when I found that I couldn't escape being a plant breeder; after a few years I discovered that I was bringing my sketchy knowledge of medicine to the test of Nature's laws and learning more about the profession in a few months at my own work than I had been able to learn in two years poring over books or listening to lectures. Nature taught me the elements of life and growth and health — the fundamentals governing everything pertaining to the body of the plant or the animal or the human being. She did not teach me everything, understand; she taught me *the fundamentals behind everything*.

Presently I was my own doctor and doctor to my men and to half the neighborhood. I saw in the plant that proper food and air and the right amount of moisture were vital necessities, but also that elimination was equally important to remove waste and used-up materials; I applied the law to human beings and made myself conversant with that essential of health. I found that I could cure sick plants, if they were worth curing, and the laws that applied in their cases were analogous to those that apply to humans. Clogged passages, closed pores, bruised roots or leaves, disordered circulatory systems in plants were all disastrous; the same was true of people or dogs or horses or house flies. So I began to watch my own pores and lungs and nasal passages and keep them open — and I invented a mixture that clogged the passages of the fly until he became a scarce commodity around my ranch.

This conviction that the basic laws were the same for both plants and animals, generally speaking, led me, of course, to a renewed curiosity about disease, health, obesity, lung troubles, exercise and diet, sleep and work, stomach troubles and diet — all the ramifications of the science of being well and fit — and I began to read books and magazine articles and pamphlets on the subjects. As a layman — a clergyman or a book-agent or a hod-carrier — I might have read libraries and made little progress; now, an active and interested student in the University of Nature, I found myself able to grasp subjects and assimilate information at one reading of the books. I met knotty points, of course, and encountered problems that were too much for me, but in the main I was able to stand on the solid ground a naturalist must occupy and to understand and digest just about everything that came under my eye. In short I had found, in Nature, the fundamentals, thoroughly mastered them, made them a part of myself, and then, turning to medicine and its discoveries, was enabled to dovetail the joints, bridge the gaps, and construct for myself a pretty substantial structure of knowledge about the science of health and disease.

If I seem to be overimpressed with my own ability I am misstating the facts. I want merely to say that the diligent student of Nature has a tremendous start over the man who is satisfied with, or can only get, a general education from books or lectures. With Nature's laws as a foundation, an intelligent man or woman can master subjects otherwise only to be learned by starting at the bottom and going right through to the end of the subject, consuming years of time. Because, in that case, you are learning Nature's universal code only in part and then only as it is twisted or interpreted or partitioned up to provide a groundwork for the particular branch of learning you are pursuing.

It is as though a sailor were only taught to reef the mainsail. Later he might be taken off that task and sent overside to paint the hull, and presently he would learn something about that. But suppose he were taught thorough seamanship, from the beginning, including every branch and department of navigation, and, not only that, but the fundamentals underlying the whole art and business of sailing a ship. With those fundamentals impressed on him he would learn handily to tie a knot, or reef a sail, or make one, or stow one, or to paint or keep watch or read the compass or steer the vessel, because he would know why these things were done and what was accomplished by doing them and what would happen if or when they weren't done, and presently you would have an able seaman, on his way up to be a mate, where the other sailor would be reefing mainsails and painting hulls till he died of old age in his hammock in the forecastle!

My study of botany was thorough and covered a number of years, but it was not until I came to plant breeding in the University of Nature that I began to go back of botany into what we call paleontology — the science of reading the story of the earth as written in fossils and remains and prints and indications that are found in the various rock formations of the ball on which we live. All too few people know how much of our knowledge of the past has been already gleaned from the rocks; there could be no more interesting theme, even for the layman. Because deductions from what fossil remains show give us an amazingly exact basis from which to reconstruct the history of life on this planet long before man's appearance on it — what some one has beautifully called 'The Manuscript of God.'

Paleobotany is the study of ancient botanical forms, habits and dispersions; the prehistoric parents of your garden flowers have some of them been found, and the slow upward progress of plant life from simpler to more complex grades has already been partly traced. If I were going to know about plants it was early evident to me that I had to know about their origins, and this led me to study paleobotany, and paleobotany being a story written in the rocks, led me to study the rocks themselves, and this brought me to a study of geology. Here, very soon, I found myself on familiar ground, because the fundamental laws of Nature were the same for crystals and conglomerates, for granites and marbles, for sandstone and shale, as for my plants; the Book of the Rocks was opened for me and plain for me to read, and again I was introduced to a fascinating and absorbing subject and was able to add it to my course of studies.

As a boy I had owned a great curiosity about chemistry and I had once acquired some test tubes, a broken retort, and a few chemicals and had performed simple experiments, greatly to the distress of my family, who were divided between anxiety lest I blow myself to bits and extreme irritation at the smells that arose from my makeshift laboratory. I was not long a plant breeder when I found it necessary to know a good deal concerning the chemical agencies which bring about growth, color, fragrance and seed-making, and here once more I discovered that my University had grounded me soundly so that chemistry was a simple thing for me to understand.

It has been said that no man could actually change the characteristics of flower or fruit, but could only add to or accentuate or, on the other hand, diminish or neutralize, tendencies already inherent in the plant. But I have proved over and over again that I could put fragrance into a flower, or remove an objectionable or disagreeable odor, that I could give a fruit the color I wanted, the texture I wanted, and the flavor I wanted. This was not done by the exercise of magic. It was done in every case by a careful study of the plant or tree concerned, and of its chemical constituents, a knowledge of what new principles would effect a change, and a careful, logical, persistent programme for introducing the new essentials into the life and body of the variety.

Air and sunshine and soil furnish the plant with all its raw materials, the heredity of the plant furnishes the habit of working up those materials, and environment supplies the varying influences that will cause the plant to reach for new things in the old raw materials and to alter or adapt its methods of manufacture within itself. In precisely the same way we humans are learning that foods have a great deal to do with our ability to perform certain work or follow certain activities, and in the last few years we have developed domestic science to the point where the cook must be something of a chemist and to

where science has entered the kitchen to stay.   Infant mortality has been decreased by the same
method that plant mortality has — by studying
the chemistry of foods and giving the infant what
it requires, which may be, often, something quite
different from the usual food or the foods of other
children of the same age or even of the same family.
Chemistry is one of our great, growingly useful
sciences; if it weren't for its rather formidable look,
thanks to the signs chemists use to denominate
various properties and elements, I expect more
people would delve into it.

Well, these are just a few of the subjects that I
have taken up in my University.   There are more
to be discussed, in my rambling fashion; for the
moment let me commend Nature to you as a teacher
not only learned and skillful, but understanding,
patient, and helpful.   To me it seems that she holds
out her hands to us, inviting us to come to her for our
lessons; that she is more anxious to teach us than
we are, usually, to be taught.   She teaches her lesser
children — all they know comes from her.   Perhaps it is too bad that we are so self-satisfied: we
have built ourselves little theories, petty beliefs,
narrow conclusions, and we learn those by rote and
pass them on from generation to generation, and
are pleased with ourselves and perfectly contented to
let the larger and broader significances and wonders
of life pass by.

One thing is sure: the conceited, self-satisfied,
bigoted man or woman, or the willful and headstrong
child can learn nothing from Nature.   She has a
strong prejudice against that sort of ignorance and

bull-headedness; if you are willing to learn and don't propose, the first day in school, to set yourself up as smarter than the mistress, you can make great progress; if you know it all you will find yourself very shortly decorated with the fool's-cap and set up on the stool in the corner, an object-lesson and a figure of scorn to every one but, perhaps and alas! — yourself.

XIV

THE science which deals with the whole order, process, and manifestation of life we call Biology; of it botany is but one small division, and of botany my own science of plant breeding is, again, a subdivision. I might have been content with my own line, but I was enormously interested in botany; I might have stopped there, but there was no stopping for me — I had to know the fundamentals of biology.

It is in the field of biology that most of the fierce battles of science are fought, because it is the science that undertakes to explain man to himself, and that is a sensitive point for all of us. I well remember the furor that was created by Darwin's 'Origin of Species,' which set forth the master's theory as to the evolutionary development of all life from lower types. If Darwin had promulgated some theory about chemistry or astronomy or geology, or even if he had confined himself to pigs or dogs, he would have gone to his death unnoticed by the most of the world, but the moment some one said that Darwin found the professors and the business men and the preachers and the saloon-keepers and farmers and laborers were descended from monkeys, they wanted to run him out of the community! Darwin did not say we were descended from monkeys, but that made no difference — it sounded something like that, and it was a good, insulting, mean sort of phrase to get warmed up over, so the fight was on!

As a matter of fact I doubt if there would be, to-

day, much of an argument between science and religion if the scientists would confine themselve to
fish and guinea-pigs and salamanders and ooze.
The trouble arises when Nature's law is shown to be
universal — to apply as well to man as to the frog
or the butterfly or the oyster. Man wants to believe
that his intelligence and his ability to think and to
have ideas removes him from what he always speaks
of as 'the lower orders'; he would much rather believe, as the old Greeks and Romans did, that his
leaders and great men were descended direct from
gods, and that he himself has natural privileges and
prerogatives that are denied dogs. As I have said
above, he certainly does have the power to adapt
himself and improve his status and station, where
the dog has a very limited capacity, but when I consider the use my dogs have made of the opportunities that were theirs, I can't feel very vainglorious
about the superiority of man.

There is no reason for a quarrel between science
and religion, if you get down to the facts of both.
The science that concerns itself with the laws of life
and the religion that concerns itself with the laws of
love can meet on every point. Biology has not solved
more than the first few of its problems, but it is still
working away, in a thousand laboratories and studies
and gardens and clinics, and one by one it is adding
to the code ordinances that are definitely demon-
strable and have been and are being demonstrated
over and over and over again. Religion has solved
many problems, too, but it is, unfortunately, inclined, like the law, to go back to precedents and
old forms and conventional rites and accepted

customs, rather than to look forward and onward; until religion keeps abreast of the times or a little ahead it will fetter itself and lose its grand and glorious opportunity for service and usefulness. That is another thing that I have learned in Nature's University!

In this connection I am reminded to say something I have wanted for a long time to say to a larger audience than the one that occasionally gathers in my home or the very dear one that sits with me around the table day by day, and that is that intolerance and bigotry are not the sole possessions of any class of men, but are very common weaknesses and faults in a large number of classes. I count among my friends hundreds of ministers and teachers, and I do not agree with all of them nor with them on all subjects. But I have never known a clergyman or a professor who could be more narrow, bigoted, and intolerant than some scientists, or pseudo-scientists. There are bigoted lawyers and intolerant business men and narrow politicians and ignorant statesmen, and it is a mistake to associate intolerance with religious sects or with reformers, because you aren't taking in enough territory.

Intolerance is a closed mind. Bigotry is an exaltation of authorities. Narrowness is ignorance unwilling to be taught. And one of the outstanding truths I have learned in my University is that the moment you reach a final conclusion on anything, set that conclusion up as a fact to which nothing can be added and from which nothing can be taken away, and refuse to listen to any new evidence, you have reached an intellectual dead-center and no-

A LATE VIEW OF THE SANTA ROSA EXPERIMENT FARM

Note rainbow corn at the left, netting over radish plants to prevent insects from assisting in a cross-pollination enterprise going on, and Shasta daisy experiments at the right

thing will start the engine again short of a charge of dynamite! Radicals, originators, daring thinkers, and free minds are the ones who explode these charges of dynamite into the machinery — I have set off a few myself, and have enjoyed a good deal of satisfaction at the resultant movement of thought, without saying anything about the fun I have had in hearing the noise, watching the smoke, and admiring the fireworks!

Ossified knowledge is a dead-weight to the world, and it does not matter in what realm of man's intellectual activities it is found. I would swap a whole cartload of precedents any time for one brand new idea. You can trace the progress of man right straight along through the centuries by setting down the inspirations of unfettered minds: Eve began it by craving the apple, Moses was an agitator and a radical, Christ was an inspired dissenter, the common people of England spelled out liberty when they violated all the old customs and scrapped all the hoary precedents by forcing King John to sign Magna Charta, Columbus shocked all the mossbacks of his time by asserting that the world was round and then demoralized them by proving it, our forefathers appalled the Houses of Parliament by proclaiming that government properly belonged to the governed, and Lincoln didn't take his notions from any books on the rights of man when he was writing the Emancipation Proclamation. The history of the world is a history of revolts, rebellions, heresies, idol-smashing, and the consignment of precedents to the everlasting junk-pile; and intolerance and any obstinate clinging to outworn doctrines, whether of religion or politics or morality or of science, are equally damning and equally damnable!

My work with plants was, of course, the work with land plants, but it opened to me another branch of the learning offered every one by the University of Nature, and that was the branch that concerns itself with water-plants and the marvelous life that abounds in the sea. How often I have dropped my cares and duties and gone to the ocean for rest and recuperation and there wandered, with little Betty Jane, my ward, or with the other Betty, my wife and companion, or sometimes alone, absorbed in the beauties and wonders of the seashore!

You will find the beaches of America generally used for one of two interests — jumping the waves or acquiring a coat of tan on the sand. How few people know the wonders of the life, so abundant and so interesting, that can be seen along the shore and among the rocks! Life in myriad forms sways or swims or idles there, from the tiniest organism clinging to a shell or a bit of moss to the fishes that dart and race hither and yonder in pursuit of food or at play; from the dainty, delicate plants to the ponderous seaweeds; from the miniature shell-life, more beautiful than jewels, to the great starfish or the giant abalone, withdrawn and with its trap open to catch a passing meal! And on the shore itself shells, brilliantly colored bits of seaweed, luminous rocks — even the individual grains of sand, especially when examined under a microscope, are an inexhaustible source of delight and inspiration.

Ichthyology — the study of fishes — and algology

— the study of sea-plants — are less familiar to us than most of the other branches of science, and yet they are equally interesting, equally fundamental, and equally comprehensible to the student, even a beginner, in the University of Nature. The laws are the same, but it is perhaps even more wonderful to contemplate the struggle for existence and the quest for a suitable environment in sea-things than in land animals and plants. To be sure sea-life was always aided by currents, and changes in the water were probably less abrupt than changes on land so that life had a better opportunity to move on or to readjust itself and readapt itself to new environmental conditions. But when you consider the unbelievable variety of life in the seas of this planet and when you realize that each must have certain conditions to make life possible and that each must find its own food and its own place in which to grow you cannot help but be impressed with the titanic nature of the struggle that has gone on through the ages from which have emerged these successful forms.

Remembering that the sun is the source of all energy and that plant life must utilize the power of the sun to transform its raw materials into living cells, you will perhaps wonder how these sea-plants can thrive without sun. The answer is that they cannot and do not: the universal law is found to be true here. Direct rays of the sun do not fall on any sea-plants except those that float on the surface, but rays of light from the sun do, and therefore you will learn that no sea-plant life exists at ocean depths where complete darkness reigns. And this will interest you, perhaps, to take a farther step and note the differences in color in the leaves of these sea-plants. In earlier chapters I dwelt on the importance of the chlorophyl granules — the green-colored cells — that you find in the leaves of all land-plants. It will appear to you that there is some mistake here, again, for these leaves are brown or reddish or even red. Nevertheless the same law applies; the fact is that the sea-plant's leaves have actually in them the same chlorophyl granules as the rose or the pine or the geranium, and that there is only a different combination of pigments, some of them abundant enough to deceive you and to make you think there is no green there. It is there because green is the color of those granules which, alone in all the marvelous laboratory of Nature, are capable of transmuting sunlight, oxygen, hydrogen and the other essential properties, into the starch and sugar necessary to the continued life of the plant.

Shells and pebbles and the sand are all equally interesting and equally they are the results of the same forces in life and subject to the same laws. The shellfish is a great example of indomitable patience, for it cannot hunt or adventure very far, and most of the shells — all of those that cling to rocks or piles — are pretty well fixed in their places and have to wait for food to come to them. The result is that they keep open day and night for business — the unwary customer is accommodated whenever he happens to come by unless the manager has drawn the blinds and locked the door while he is consuming the last visitor!

Here are a few suggestions of the fascinating world that lies all about us in Nature. I have not attempted to cover the whole ground; the field of science is illimitable and every one can find in it something to interest him and something from which he can learn valuable lessons for his own employment and good use. Once started in the University of Nature the humblest beginner, no matter whether he matriculates with honors from some lower school or just slips in the back way without any certificates or diplomas whatever, can soon find himself, and in no time at all he will begin to correlate what he learns, will begin to commit to memory some of the simpler laws and will begin to be impressed with what I have been writing about in these papers — the interdependence of all the children of Nature and the close parallel there is between her laws for man and those for plants or animals, fishes or insects or stars.

There is another aspect of this universal education which is free to all in Nature's University that I have not touched on — the fact that it is the magic key that unlocks the door for you to an understanding of and a sympathy with all the great minds of your time. I do not suppose any man of these days has had visits from more people, nor from people of more widely distributed sorts and professions and interests than I, and yet I have been able to converse with all of them and to understand what they were saying, even about some highly specialized work of their own, and to be interested in them and find them interested in me.

I have surprised physicians and surgeons by talking with them about the human body and human ailments, and by being more or less up-to-date in their chosen field. Partly this was, of course, because I studied medicine at twenty, but mainly it was because I was interested and because my observations were based on immutable laws that no school or branch or variety of doctoring could escape. There are a good many quacks in the medical profession, just as there are some in the law, some in the clergy, some among business men, and probably one or two in the plant-breeding line. But I have never had much patience with the effort of the older medical schools to arrogate to themselves all the authority as regards sickness and health. I do not believe in permitting every barber or organ player who wants to hang out a shingle to practice medicine or attempt cures, but I do assert that there is room for those who believe in stretching the muscles and readjusting the backbone and giving internal baths and in proper diet or the use of water in ill-health as well as for those who rely on nostrums and drugs and pellets and pills and serums. I have been treated by allopaths, naturopaths, hydropaths, osteopaths, and calf-paths in my time, and I have found that the best man is the one who best aids Nature to a readjustment of your body — that it is Nature herself who does the heavy work. Give her a chance, boost her over the rough places, provide her with a certain amount of raw materials, and don't hamper her with your obstinacy or hamstring her with your own bad habits and presently she will be running the job at the old stand, and doing it pretty efficiently, too!

I have expressed myself about education, on various occasions, and have had something to say that educators with open minds would listen to, because the training of the human plant is very closely related to the training of the garden plant or the tree. People have scolded me and abused me and scoffed at me, but I find them coming closer and closer all the time to a rational, natural method of education, which is the only thing for which I ever contended. It has been objected that I have no children and therefore have no right to discuss this sacred subject of schooling for the young, but I observe that about ninety-six per cent of all our teachers, from the bottom up, are spinsters or bachelors, and I can't see how I can be made out any more of an amateur than they.

Did you ever think what is the most pliable and the most precious product of all the ages? Not pigs, mules, books, locomotives, cotton or corn, but children. Children respond to ten thousand subtle influences which would leave no more impression on a plant or on most grown-ups than they would on a sphinx; children are the greatest individualists we know — they are all different and all sensitive and easily moulded and led. This is part of Nature's scheme to get variations; the different temperaments, inclinations, strengths and weaknesses of your little ones ought to be encouraged, capitalized on, and encouraged. Instead we pour them all into one mould, like steel wire fed through a pin-making machine, and when they are standardized so that you can hardly tell their minds apart we expect them to go out into the world and make something of themselves. If they do it is in spite of their education instead of because of it.

Man has by no means reached the ultimate goal toward which he is traveling, and the growing children are the ones who must take the forward steps, as they come to manhood. If we have tried to make them into a pattern of ourselves progress is impossible and Nature's aim by so much defeated. Let them drink in all that is pure and sweet, don't stuff platitudes, sentimentalism or dogma down their throats, and whatever you do, don't frighten them either of dark corners in the house or of dark corners in life! Let Nature teach them the lessons of good and proper living, put them in touch with the best contacts you know, let them absorb truth and beauty and human brotherhood as the plant does sunshine and dew, and those children will grow to be the best men and women.

Closely related to education, nowadays, as well as to an increasingly wide field of other human activities is the science of psychology, and here my education in Nature's university has made me able to understand formulated laws and formulate a few premises of my own. Among my visitors have been several of the soundest psychologists of our time, and I have been intensely interested in them and in their points of view. We have had a working knowledge of psychology much longer than we have had a name for the science. I have found able psychologists among callers from East India where they have thought for centuries along lines that we commonly consider metaphysical. But the basis for much of their teaching was the influence of our sub-conscious minds on the things we thought and did and said, and no matter what they called that influence they have long been able to get results through application of the same principles that are taught in schools of salesmanship, practiced in psycho-analysis, or used as a basis for the examination of the minds and intellectual capacities of men and women or boys and girls to-day.

I believe that we have, perhaps, just about reached the end of this age of mechanical and chemical progress which has been so astounding as to change the whole face of things, even in my own lifetime; I think it not unlikely that there will come later an age when science will concentrate on the wonders of the mind of man and on the subjects that we now consider mystical and psychic. We have five senses, but all around us we see evidences that there may be a sixth sense, or some additional power of getting impressions and knowledge from without by another means than smelling, tasting, seeing, hearing, or feeling. Undoubtedly here we have a great field to work in — a field now almost untouched. We may some day find psychology only the first of a great body of sciences concerning themselves with what is now but hinted at in the present stage of this department of knowledge.

A world to which many of my inclinations call me is the world of art. From my earliest days I wanted to express myself and my thoughts and what I saw through some medium other than speech, and I wrote news notes for our local papers, tried my hand at an essay or two, sketched with pencil, and finally painted a few small pictures. One of them, viewed

now with the kindly, prejudiced eye of a man past
seventy, especially kindly and prejudiced when that
man was the boy of sixteen who painted it, seems
quite good; it hangs on my bedroom wall and once
in a while I am tempted to get a brush and some color
and see if there is any way I can improve the legs of
the cows standing in the stream in the foreground.
I do not suppose I would have made a great artist,
but I had a love for the work and only a few years
ago, when I was tired and needed relaxation, I
copied a picture that pleased me in a magazine, and
did it in oil, too.

What I am leading up to is that I have always had
a sense of color, and this sense has been sharpened
and refined by my long association with the canvases
Nature paints. Artists have said that I had an
astonishing understanding of color; if I have it is not
only because of my predilection that way but because in Nature's University the art course is by no
means the least important or valuable one. Nature
has taught man all he knows about art — or Art, if
that is the way you prefer to write it — and you will
observe that, when painters become too academic
and get too far away from fundamentals, some young
genius appears who has gone straight to Nature herself for his source of inspiration, and there is a great
swing back to a simple, natural, direct painting,
without any bungling or frills that come only from
the schools.

My writing I have kept up from boyhood; and
though I was so busy for forty years that I had little
time for records, since then I have set down many of
my experiences, observations, and thoughts. When

I needed to eke out my small income in the earlier years with outside revenue I could always sell a paper or two to some newspaper or magazine; in addition to this I have accumulated a vast store of manuscripts on my work and methods, enough to make a five-foot shelf of books, I suppose, that I have never published. Not only have I been urged to write by the importance of what I had to say about my work, but my innate impulse to express myself was always active in me, and, finally, Nature's University fairly pushes a man to his desk and a pen and a pad of paper because there are so many things observed that cry out to be written down.

All these varied and ranging interests of mine — of a naturalist living close to the things of Nature and impressed and inspired and enthused by them — have made me what I suppose you would be able only to call a cosmopolite — a dweller in all the world — even though I have not gone outside the immediate neighborhood of my home in Santa Rosa more than a score of times in my life. I have been in touch with the world — my interests have never been local. I have had the world brought to me by visitors from every land, and from every walk of life, and I have kept abreast of things through the common interest I had with all — my interest in Nature and her ways.

Precious friendships have come to me in this fashion. To meet and know really great minds has been one of the keenest satisfactions of my life; none of my friendships have been measured by any other standard save the standard of true fineness and sterling character. Without exception the men

who have come to me and with whom I have built
up friendships have been fellow-students of mine in
the University of Nature. Because it was in the
language of that school that I spoke, and it was only
users of that tongue who could understand me or
speak to me. The great-souled humanist, Thomas
Edison, whose whole life has been spent in my University, and whom very few people know as he is,
was my friend long before we met; his work, at first
glance so entirely different from mine, was the same
as mine, for where I worked with plants he worked
with forces and elements, but both of us to the one
end that Nature's laws might be codified, interpreted, and set to work for the betterment of mankind. Edison has chained the lightning and trained
the illimitable energies of the earth to lessen man's
burden; approaching the subject from an entirely
different angle he came to fundamentals as surely
and as straightly as I did, because both of us were
nothing except as we sat at Nature's feet and learned
her lessons and applied them under her laws.

There is no other door to knowledge than the door
Nature opens; there is no truth except the truths we
discover in Nature. We pride ourselves on our un-
matched commercial and mechanical progress, but
behind all business, all industry, all wealth are
natural laws; the pity is that so few men take time
to go back to original sources for interest and information, but that they are content to skim the
surface, take their learning second-hand, and ignore
the beauty and sublimity and serenity that are to be
absorbed from the infinite expressions of life as
Nature unfolds them before us, if we will look and

listen and attend. In every man, no matter how ignorant or how hurried or how driven or how successful in other lines, there is a dormant love of Nature and natural things; it would take very little of the time you crowd so full of everything else for you to breathe in some of the incense of gardens, to feast your eyes on the calm and changeless beauty of the hills, to rest your bodies on the quiet beauty of the earth, and to heal your souls in the perfect serenity of some unbroken wilderness.

Well, I can only write, as well as I am able, a prospectus of the institution for you: if you are looking for an education I can only recommend my own and tell my own experience. I can only say to you, as I am trying to say in these papers, that what I have had you may have, that what I have enjoyed you may enjoy, that what I have learned you may learn, and that it is all free, all open, all generously bestowed on man — that, whatever your preparation, whatever your age, whatever your early training or present occupation, you are welcome now or at any time in the future to enter on a new and incredible adventure by matriculating, without money and without price, in The University of Nature!

XV

I HAD a grand house-cleaning once.

It was always a habit with me to save the bulk of my letters, partly for reference and partly because a letter seems to me so much a part of the writer that destroying it is a painful task; I started by putting them away in packages, in bundles, in boxes — I finally had to do them up in bales and stuff them into hogsheads until at last there was nothing for it but to store them in the loft of my big old barn.

Then I needed the loft. Something had to go, so I put two young men at the job of sorting the ten years' accumulation, taking off such names and addresses as might be useful later and then burning the lot.

It took them the better part of a week, and according to their rough calculation that loft held eighty-five thousand letters!

When they had finished, they came to me with a paper box full of unused postage stamps, many of them foreign and several of large denomination.

'We took those out of the letters,' they said.

And when I had had them counted those stamps totaled enough to pay the wages of the two boys twice over. They had been sent to pay for seeds, for return postage, for small bills, and the like, and had been overlooked when the letters were read.

After that I tried to keep my correspondence cleaned up all the time, but, pshaw! it wasn't any use. I suppose I have accumulated in the last ten years fully as many letters as were destroyed in that wholesale house-cleaning of 1914; it seems to me I have disposed of pretty nearly all my mail as soon as it was answered and the business it concerned was finished, but now, looking through the house and the offices and the barn in search of things to jog my memory for these chapters, I find that I am again like a needle in a haystack of letters!

I wonder, contemplating them, how I have contrived to make time to attend to them, and yet I don't believe any friendly, courteous request, any business communication, any letter of inquiry, any application for information, a job, a loan or a recommendation, or even any missive blaming me for the poor state of civilization or cussing me for something I have said or have not done, has ever crossed my desk, in sixty years, without being given some sort of reply.

We had a heavy old bore visiting us once who never said anything or thought anything or did anything without cocking his head on one side and asking himself just how a mention of that thing said or thought or done would look when it appeared in his biography. Somehow that angle of the matter never struck me at all. Maybe I was too busy or maybe too independent or maybe too direct in my habit of mind to be concerned; at any rate I doubt that they will get much out of my letters that will be worth preserving for their fine literary style or for the bits of scandal hidden away in them, or for any of the other qualities that appear to make a man's letters worth printing after he has ceased to write letters for all time to come!

No, the biggest interest will be found in the letters written to me.

I have mentioned some of them before in these chapters — the letters from collectors in scattered parts of the world who have sent me seeds and bulbs and cuttings for experimentation, and perhaps these are the most interesting and informative of the great mass of correspondence I have had, because they tell of adventures near and far, of the countries where the writers lived, of the customs and habits of the people, of the botanical and climatic wonders — they are, in short, a sort of travel series, reading which one can go around the world in seven hours, and from pole to pole in an evening!

But there have been many other interesting and instructive letters, and also there have been callers at my door who have added to the pleasure of existence for me and have given me about the only contacts I have had with the world of people and events.

The mailbag and the doorbell! You who live in big cities, who travel about the world, who go to the theater one night, to the opera the next, to a lecture course, to great dinners, to clubs where famous men gather around the fireplace or the table and swap stories of their lives and experiences and opinions — all you who move about and have your contacts with a great mass of people as your daily portion, may never have tasted the joy of knowing the world through the mailbag and the doorbell. It is not so bad a way: it has this advantage over yours that, whereas you know what is coming and can choose what you want to indulge in and can determine for yourselves pretty largely what each day will bring in the way of contacts, I have been so tied by my work and my interests that whatever I have had has come to me, and has come generally without my asking for it, or knowing of it in advance, or having any idea of what it would be when it did come.

The faithful, patient, smiling mailman (one of our best friends and most tireless servants, but one we too often accept as a cog in the machine of life, and give no consideration to as a human being and a friend!) has been coming my way ever since I started my nursery business in Santa Rosa back in 1878; he has walked, or he has ridden a bicycle or he has driven a lean old horse or a fat and chubby pony, or he has come in an automobile, and he has brought the world to my desk, rain and shine, summer and winter, early and late ever since that date, and made me smile, or laugh, or thrill with satisfaction, or puff with pride, or weep in sympathy, or cuss a little, in a mild way, or pound my desk and explode in good, old-fashioned, satisfying 'downeast' vernacular. He has been the principal line of communication between me and the great things and the fine people of the earth, and I am grateful to him, and have told him so, time and again, and man after man as the job passed down a long line of successive mailmen on my route.

I have seen a great change in letters in my time. The old art of letter-writing seems to have died out, and more and more I have noticed that a letter is the mere bones of a body that might have been breathed full of color, fragrance, friendliness and satisfaction. That, of course, is part of our modern development;

the main thing now is to use the fewest possible words, make ourselves clear in the business — and file copies for use in case a lawsuit comes up! There isn't much romance in that kind of letter-writing, and there never can be!

Taken generally, my mailbag has contained letters and papers and clippings and books more interesting and colorful and romantic to me when taken together, as a cross-section of the times and a survey of the world, than as separate, individual human documents. If a body has a mind to, he can get a pretty interesting and valuable notion of human nature from letters. The politician is there who wants to win an office, or to hang on to the one he has, or to make a showing so he will be promoted, or to clutch at an appointment just before he is beaten at the polls; he seldom wants you to think about the good of the nation or the state, or to ask for your help in a worthy cause, or to make it possible for you to find a way out of your own troubles or difficulties. The reformer is there with his scheme for making every one better overnight, in violation of all Nature's laws and of the facts of history and biology; the promoter is there with his plan for giving you something for nothing, provided you make a small advance to him of the something, in cold, hard cash or negotiable paper!

The idealist is there with a dream of finer things — usually a little impractical as to his machinery; the unsought friend is there warning you against somebody or something you had no idea of exposing yourself to; the jealous man is there, so afraid something you do or say will seem to cast a shadow on his zealously guarded reputation or dizzily erected structure of complacence; the failure is there who wants to know how he can succeed by some simple process like saying 'Open, Sesame!' or waving a wand over the black bag of his own incompetence; the beggar is there who is sure your well-known kindliness and tender heart will prompt you to help him and his invalid wife take a sea-trip, when you know that they live better than you do and have two grown-up children in the family who don't seem to be contributing much to this nautical enterprise! — they are all there, and thousands more, just as you find them in life, but a little off their guard in letters and much more likely to give themselves away through the very anxiety they show to make out a good case for themselves.

But that is only one side of the picture. The big, busy, royal soul is there who takes a minute from his hurried day to tell you that you are doing well at your job, and more power to you! The true friend is there who knows you are rushed and so won't come to see you, or take up your time calling, but who must say that he loves you and wishes you well and will do anything you want him to do, if the occasion arises when you need him. The sincere admirer is there, clumsy with words, perhaps, but unable to resist the urge to say that you are appreciated in some quarters, anyhow, and that you have done him good — or done her good, perhaps — by something you have written or said or accomplished in your own field and fashion.

The shut-ins are there — the sick, the maimed, the blind or deaf, reaching out their hands to you and thanking you for what you are trying to do; the old are there, tired from the struggle but sweetened and mellowed by their experiences in it, and glad to say a cheery word or to give you a bit of sound, old-time advice, or to suggest something you would never think of until you, too, came ninety and could look dispassionately on life and see a lot of things the young folks of sixty or seventy miss.

And the children are there, in thousands!

DEAR MR. LUTHER BURBANK:

I read in the paper that you were sick. I hope you will get better. In reading we have been reading your books and I like them better than any other books. My name is Mildred and I and two other friends are going to have a flower garden this summer and try mixing the pollen. I am in the sixth grade. The thing I like best is to plant flowers and watch them grow.

Yours truly
MILDRED VASCONCELLOS

DEAR FRIEND:

We are the children of the seventh grade of the Clara Barton School and we want to write to tell you how much we like you and how wonderful we think it is that you wanted to work with flowers and make them better. We have a garden in a vacant lot near the school and grow only the Luther Burbank seeds.

Our teacher, Miss Neilsen, takes us on trips on Saturdays sometimes to study the wild flowers and the trees in the timber north of Lake Ocatong; when we are there we wonder what you would say if you could go with us and tell us about the things we do not know about flowers and nature.

We hope you are well and that your flowers and trees will be more beautiful to you and to us all the time.

Your friends
SEVENTH GRADE

DEAR FRIEND:

A man lectured in our town last year about you and how you cross flowers by putting pollen on them so I tried it with a sunflower and this spring my seeds came up and I want to tell you they were great! You never saw so many different kinds of sunflowers and the chickens didn't know whether they were sunflowers or some new kind of weed. I wish you could see them. I am eleven years old and I wish I could do the kind of things you do and I am going to try and get smart enough to do the same kind of things when I grow up.

LEWIS LENSTADT

I am sending you a snap-shot of me and my little sister standing by the sunflowers.

If I had a room that was as big as my love for children is big, I would have it filled from floor to ceiling with that sort of letter, for there have been enough of them, and they are still coming. I never failed to answer them, or have them answered, and I never felt the time was wasted, or the stationery or the trouble. My whole life has been spiced and enriched by my acquaintance with little folks, and I have always felt fortunate in having them for my friends and happy in their admiration and confidence and esteem, because they are genuine, they are true, they understand and love Nature, and they have no motives except motives of kindliness and interest and enthusiasm!

Kind thoughts and a wish to be of service beget kindness and generosity all the world over, I have found. People always felt somehow that I was well disposed toward every one and my work spoke for itself, so that I was early the recipient of thousands of the most sincere and friendly letters. It is doubtful if more than one tenth of one per cent of the correspondents ever reached Santa Rosa or the gardens, yet many of them wrote now and again over a long period of years. As time went on and my business activities, of a very diversified sort, waxed great the notes from old friends, only known through the agency of the mailman yet nevertheless dear to me and usually recognized before the envelopes were opened, were thankfully received and fully enjoyed.

They traveled, too, these friends of mine, into strange and fascinating corners of the globe: I have two scrapbooks full of picture postal cards that some of them sent me as they went, so that I got a breath of air and a glimpse of beauty from every land through their kindness and thoughtfulness. To me many of their names are more familiar than the names of my own neighbors in Santa Rosa; I learned their characters and dispositions and interests through their letters and notes to me; I could tell which man was inclined to a short temper, which to an over-generous heart, which to a love of art and music, which to a cool and business-like appraisal of values of life, which to sentiment — and which to gushing sentimentality. I vow I could tell you more about many of my correspondents than you could tell about any but your intimates, because a mailbag friend puts himself down, in the end, pretty clearly on paper and draws a picture of himself for the discerning to see, even though he may be writing only of external things and may scarcely mention himself.

The concern of these distant friends over my health was always touching and warming to me. After a while I began to be watched by the newspapers, and a bad cold in the head would get me as much space as the introduction of a new fruit destined to bring blessing and profit to the race for a thousand years! This curiosity about me — my habits, my eating, my home life, my thoughts, my aches and pains — had the result of bringing to me rivers of letters. I find that, by going through the correspondence hastily, I can almost reconstruct the story of my life and that there are brought to my mind innumerable incidents and small sicknesses and trifling business matters that I have myself long since forgotten.

Thus, along about 1894 and thereafter I had a worry that made me sleepless and ruined my digestion; in the letters of those years I find scores prescribing for me, offering remedies, urging dietary changes, and generally fussing over me as though I were in the last stages of collapse! And what a variety of cures! If I had tried one half of them I would have despoiled the back room of the local pharmacy; if I had experimented with any considerable proportion of the remedies proposed for sleeplessness I would have been up all night putting myself to sleep! And as for diets, there is no hotel in the land that would not have been ruined in a week had I dropped in there as a guest and begun to order the variety of foods prescribed for me by my anxious friends!

My mailbag was a curious medley of voices from the outside world. Almost every one wanted something — in the humblest and most thoughtful way, usually, and with no intention of being a nuisance or causing me vexation or trouble. Often, of course, they wanted impossible things: I don't know why they should have thought that I was a combination of King Solomon, Cambridge University, and an information desk, but apparently they did!

From one mail, chosen at random, I glean the following:

I trust that I may write you concerning a peach tree grown in my backyard. This may be of no consequence but it is unusual for a natural tree and those who have tasted the fruit pronounce it exceptional. If it is true I should like to make it profitable to me and to society, but I am unfamiliar with methods of determining the quality of the fruit or for commercializing it. Therefore I am sending you a can of the fruit and a few twigs which are commencing to bud.

Approximately what might be the value of such a tree? Should it be sold outright to a nursery, and what steps would one take to prove the value to a nurseryman and, when proved, to sell it?

I shall be very anxious to hear the result of your analization of the fruit.

That was a stumper, because the fruit was canned and there was little about it to distinguish it from other peaches; moreover, the twigs died on the way, so my 'analization' didn't get very far. But at any rate, this query was in my own line, and I could reply with a show of intelligence.

But look at this one:

I enclose herewith a typewritten copy of my book on The Seat of the Power of Cognition. This has been read by a prominent physician and has his approval on all questions of human physiology.

I would appreciate your reading this and giving me a frank opinion concerning it. Whatever you say will be considered confidential and I hope you will not hesitate to point out any errors you may discover.

I was always receiving that kind, and as for books on every subject under the sun, thousands of them printed at the expense of the writers, I could fill a good-sized library with them!

What we used to call 'cranks' swarmed to me through my mailbag. If you had plenty of time and patience you could get a certain amount of amusement trying to make out what it was they were talking about — and sometimes you succeeded. It was as fascinating as the cross-word puzzle and only a little more difficult! In this mail I am writing of there was the following:

MY DEAR FELLOW FRIEND AND SCIENTIST:

It is God's will that I have the privilege of presenting a message concerning the two foremost flowers of the Earth — 'The Lily and the Poppy' drafting one on the other, which symbolizes one of Peace on Earth and Good Will Toward Men — one of which will place the world to know a new standard and one of which will elevate the heart and mind to balance in a more perfect atmosphere — in that source of which is — all harmonious. It is all thought and mind that spirit determines, guides and directs. It is a crossed specimen between the Chinese opium poppy and the Egyptian Calla White Lily — or the Lily of the Nile, Cape of Good Hope.

That geographical hybridization finished me! It looked as though I hadn't been grounded sufficiently on the new plane to tackle metaphysical botany of that variety, so I wrote a note, I suppose, thanking the writer and expressing a devout wish that he wouldn't come again!

But here was something to take the eye! The heavy, substantial-looking, impressive stationery that foreigners commonly use always did fascinate me; they accuse me of putting a good many letters into the safe just because of the looks of them. And this was one. It came in a big white envelope, with a seal and a whole collection of Austrian stamps on it, and was addressed:

To Mr.

BURBANK

Botanist and Scientific Planter,

U.S. Nordamerika

The mailmen had made a good guess on that vague direction, and here was the letter in my hand, reading thus:

DEAR MR.

BURBANK,

J got your address from a friend of mine and should like to ask of you a favor. Having since some years a fancy in growing cactus plants in hot houses, J will start now in a greater style and secured already land and hot houses. For the beginning J need some seeds of the adhering list, altogether about 200 gramms, which you may mail by sample without value. Later, if J come more in business, J intend to import by your help whole plants. You may be convinced that J will cover all the expenses you may have.

In the hope that you will trust me and do me the favor, J remain with the kindest greetings.

That letter was the beginning of a pleasant friendship and some small profit on both sides, I hope.

The next started generally and ended up particularly — a characteristic I observed in many letters of this nature. It ran:

For years in Norway, my native country, I taught Natural History. I love animals and I admire and wonder about plants. True we do not appreciate them as we ought to, was my thought then, as it still is. They are able to teach us all about a beautiful life, but most people do not learn their language. What they miss by that they never will even know.

And now my old soul wants your sun shining on it, Dear Mr. Burbank. Would you please let your secretary kindly tell me if there would be any possibility for me to get any kind of work in or around Santa Rosa.

That was what it was all leading up to! And yet, on second thought, perhaps I am doing the writer an injustice. It was a kindly letter, well meant and well written, and although I wasn't able to help the writer, I felt a little warmed around the heart, I'm sure, by the interest shown and the confidence she had in me, whom she had never seen and only vaguely heard of, perhaps.

There was always at least one present, large or small, most of them sent without any hope of return or expectation of reward or reciprocation of any sort. It was embarrassing, at times, yet plainly these people, whom I have never known at all, were actuated by generous and kindly motives in sending things to me. There was a package and a letter in this typical mailbag I am writing of. The letter read:

I have long been an admirer of your successful work and as a small token of my esteem I am forwarding a box of my candy which I trust reaches you in good condition.

My parents came from Germany many years ago where my father learned the confectioner's art. I was born in the business and like yourself have tried always to improve my work.

I trust you will accept this small gift with the feeling it comes from a friend.

There was a feeling of brotherhood in that statement of his that he also had always tried to make his work better — and the family assured me that he had succeeded after the sample had been passed around and tested by the experts there present!

An Oregon man's letter came next:

I have been particularly interested in what is known locally as the willow-herb, that grows here along streams, in the open woods, and especially in burns. It is so abundant that it crowds out the grasses and is hard to eradicate. It would be a big thing if it could be crossed with something to make it a useful plant, and I have been wondering if any cross would be possible that would develop for commercial use the abundant silky fibers that cover the seed-capsules. I trust that I may hear from you on this subject.

It was a good thought, and though I did not have time to go into the experiment, I have no doubt that the writer was a man of intelligence and that there was the germ of an idea somewhere in his question. It is from such beginnings that most of our great discoveries have been made and most of our important improvements have sprung, and I was never too busy to encourage people who took time to think for themselves and who showed an interest in nature and her gifts to man.

The day wouldn't have been complete without something like this:

Are you available for an address before our annual

Teachers' Convention? We would make our dates suit your convenience and would like to be informed as to your preference for a subject and as to your usual charge.

I could answer that without hesitation. I almost never made addresses, I never traveled far from home, I had no preferences as to subject so long as they would let some one else do the lecturing, and my usual charge was a million dollars an hour, which was the least I would take for subjecting myself to the agony of standing up before an audience and trying to remember what it was my wife had suggested I should say! So there was a message easy to reply to.

Back on my own territory again with the next!

DEAR MR. BURBANK:
The cattlemen in this country have all gone broke all on account of a weed that the cattle eat. It has occurred to me that possibly you might be able to help them get rid of the weed.

This weed or loco as we call it causes the cattle and horses that eat it to go crazy. They will eat it when it is green or dry. But it affects them worse when they eat it dry.

It grows during the fall, winter and early spring, then it dries up. It resembles alfalfa some and they tell me that it belongs to the same family.

If you are interested to study this weed to see if you can find something that will kill it or find some way to improve it so that cattle can eat it as a food I would like to hear from you.

I had previously made some investigation of this loco weed and had given two or three Western experiment stations hints as to possible methods of procedure, but I had to leave it to them to carry out the project. As a matter of fact it looks pretty hopeless to me. You see, when you have a weed or a varmint or a family of men that has run to seed for a long time and has been poisonous and noxious and dangerous, you have fixed those qualities in the heredity firmly, and it would take more than a generation or two to improve them and to make them useful and ornamental and law-abiding.

The loco weed and the poison-oak and the weasel and the ground squirrel and the confirmed thief are developments — not accidents. You can't put the blame on the individual, and you can't do very much to change the individual unless you take him young and give him an entirely different environment and work with him and train him and be ready to put a barbed-wire fence around him if he shows signs of breaking off the reservation again. We have loco weeds, in our literature as well as on our prairies, that would be better rooted out and burned, but we have let them go on growing up there, and we have encouraged them and given them a chance, and now we can't turn around in a day and suppress the sex stories and eliminate the sensation from our newspapers and expurgate our vicious novels by a simple wave of the hand. The loco weed looks good to eat, and the suggestive novel shows off well on the newsstand, but both of them are deceiving and cause the consumer to go off his head: it is going to be a job to get rid of either one of the weeds, but some day we will take hold manfully and do it, whether by grafting in some better stock or by rolling up our sleeves and burning out the whole infested area to the grass-roots!

Land, how I do ramble on!

The dearest treasures the mailbag contained were letters from tried and true friends — common folks and unknown to fame, as well as men and women with names known the world over — whom some accident or chance brought into contact with me and whom some common interest made my brethren. A friendship like the one correspondence brought me with Judge Ben Lindsey, the Denver jurist who put a new face on law proceedings concerning women and children, was worth more than minted gold to me; I made my friends largely through the mail.

There are points to that method. Because, while it insures your taking on just about as many friends as you can reasonably be entitled to, you are at perfect liberty to end a friendship when it seems to lag or when the distant acquaintance shows symptoms of being a bore or a drag, and there are no hard feelings or recriminations on either hand. Certainly you can screen the chaff from the wheat in this fashion. Think what a boon a post-office department would have been to old Job!

XVI

IF I had had the time, during my life, to do all the visiting I would like to have done, I might be able to write a volume or two on the great and learned and inspired characters of our day; as it is I have enough friends to make me proud and happy, though I don't suppose I could add much to your store of information about them, because always my visiting hours had to be cut to the minimum and there were hundreds who came whom I would like to have chinned with by the hour who only got about five minutes. It was always that way: almost from the very first I found more work than I could do, and callers had to be restricted both in number and in minutes allowed.

And yet I have had some marvelous friendships and have squeezed out time enough for some deep and lasting intimacies. The late Judge S. F. Leib, of San José, a lawyer and horticulturist and a splendid, wise man, and Dr. David Starr Jordan, president emeritus of Stanford University, were two of the men I was most glad to see and with whom I could be certain to enjoy a pleasant hour or half-day whenever they would come. By the same token they came seldom and cut their stays short; I did the same when I went to see them, so we were mutually helpful and agreeable, and our friendships never suffered from overindulgence.

But there have been hundreds who have rung my doorbell and with whom I have walked in my gardens. What did we talk about? What did they say? I don't remember. Only in their friendship and their affection were they different from the thousands of others who came. They were as interested and absorbed in the work that they saw going on and in the results of that work in bed and greenhouse and orchard row as — well, as the children who came. Because, in Nature's presence, we are all children, nothing more, and honors and names and purses lose their significance and importance and are forgotten and only the awe and marvel in our hearts remain.

My doorbell gave me contact with the great, the wise, the mighty; it brought me face to face with the beautiful and enchanting women of my day; it called me to speak to little children; it summoned me to answer the questions of the curious, the eager, the modest, the bold, the amateur and the scientist, the teacher and the pupil, the greatest bores in Creation and — Harry Lauder!

A lean, brown man rang that doorbell one day, and when I answered it he told me he was a snake specialist. He knew more about snakes than any man living, I suppose, not from books or microscopes or laboratory examination, but from living with them, catching them, watching them, making pets of them. He was on the trail, he said, of a new species of snake — and there hadn't been a new species discovered, I think he said, in twenty years. He was interested in my flowers, but I don't think he got much out of me because I, on the other hand, was so interested in his snakes! In leaving he said I would hear from him — and just the other day I did. He had found his new snake, and, with my permission, was going to name it for me! I have had many things named for me — from schools to pickaninnies — but I am as proud of the Burbank Silver Striped snake as of anything on my list!

A sunburned man came one day with a pack on his back and his shoes worn through, and carrying in his hand a very handsome lily plant. He was a clerk, he said, in ill health and taking a long vacation. As he had little money he had decided to travel afoot; he had gone from San Francisco way up into Oregon, and there had discovered this lily. It was new to him, and he thought, he told me, of an old lady living in San Diego, a thousand miles from where the flower was found, who had once been kind to him and who loved flowers. He would take it to her, he decided, walking the whole distance. But when he tried, he found that it would not go into his pack without danger of killing it, so he was carrying it, from Oregon to San Diego, a thousand miles of hill and plain, mountain and waste, in his hand! He had stopped and rung my doorbell to ask me what the lily was, and when I told him it was a rare and beautiful Darlingtonia and very frail, I thought he would cry for joy.

There was a great ringing of the bell once, but the ringer seemed to lose heart and become frightened, for when I went to answer I found her halfway out on the porch looking pretty shy. It was a little girl on her way to school, and behind her was a group of them.

'Hello!' I said, in my doorway. 'Is this a committee?'

The others looked at the first. She was spokes-
man. She colored and hemmed and hawed, but
finally she got at the matter.

'The boys won't let us cross the street,' she said,
gaining some confidence as she went. 'So we told
them we'd come and tell Mr. Burbank on them.'

That was it. I put on my severest face, led them
out the gate, frowned at the boys, and piloted the
little group of timid maidens over. When I returned,
the boys watched me closely. Was I going to turn
and rend them, or was I going to lecture, or was I
going to call the police?

I said: 'It is fun to hear girls squeal, isn't it,
boys? But why don't you pick on some of the big
girls next time?'

They went off, whooping that they would.

Children are always ringing my doorbell, and I
think it gives off a more tinkling and merry peal
to their touch than to that of any sober-sided gray-
beard or tailored princeling or learned professor!

The people who bring strange or new plants to my
door are numerous; what might surprise you is the
number who have come asking me to prescribe for
sick plants — and often bringing the patient! Those
who want advice about gardening, or names of their
plants or wild-flowers, or suggestions as to border-
plants or ornamental shrubs are legion, but of
course it is impossible to help them, with my hands
so full with my experiments. I can always make a
little time, though, for the passionate flower-lovers
who come — especially for country- and mountain-
women, in their plain, worn dresses, with their hair
awry, perhaps, and their hands roughened with

work, but with beauty in their hearts and love of wild things and of Nature shining in their eyes! They bring me into intimate touch, constantly, with the heights and the spaces that I have always loved, and sometimes I steal half an hour to sit and listen to them talk of their homes and their hills, and am refreshed and helped by them and cheered by their visits.

There are two stock phrases used by miscellaneous visitors that sound new to them, of course, but that have grown very old at home.

'I couldn't leave Santa Rosa without being able to say that I saw Luther Burbank,' is one of them; the other is: 'I've come a long way to see Luther Burbank.' That last was a strong statement, until you examined it. I felt sort of guilty about not giving a minute to a man or a party that had come a long way to see me, until, by chance, I found that that 'long way' was as likely to be the fifty miles from San Francisco as it was the five thousand from Australia, and after that I had to be impressed by something more than the plea of immeasurable distances traversed!

Perhaps the visitors who have embarrassed me most — though I tried never to let them see it — have been the young ladies who have brought me their beaus for inspection before saying Yes or No to the fateful question. I don't know where I got the reputation of being an infallible judge of prospective husbands, though it was probably by word of mouth, the news spreading among girls of marriageable age with an amazing speed. I do not know, either, whether what I have said has ever discouraged a girl from going ahead with the investment; I'm inclined to doubt it. On the other hand, if I admit that the specimen trotted out seems to measure up to my idea of a running mate for double harness turn-outs I am immediately voted the greatest man in the world, and the smartest, and in due course of time am sure to have a baby named for me, if it turns out that the baby can take my name with regard to the fitness of things. Even that did not discourage one proud young mother, and somewhere in the world to-day there is a girl toting around everywhere she goes the unwieldy handle of 'Lutherine,' though I certainly hope she absolves me from responsibility for the hybridization of the name or else has long since decided to call herself Eliza Ann!

Outside of business men and buyers and scientists and insurance agents and the like, these are typical of my visitors at the home in Santa Rosa. Thousands have come who have not rung the doorbell, at all, but who have walked about the gardens on the street and looked in over the fence, which I built low so that they could see all there was to see. Most of them are satisfied, but there was a time when hundreds every year were not and would make some pretext or find some excuse to push in or to call to me or to the men, so that, in time, they became a real menace to the business. I put up signs that discouraged them, finally. I said that they could have an interview at so much a minute! After that they seemed less anxious to interrupt.

There is no getting cross with such folks, though. Their interest is great — their hearts are kindly. They can't realize that a minute to each visitor would mean an average of an hour a day and that an hour a day would be two and a half working days out of each month in a place where every minute counts and neither health nor strength will permit of any additional strain on a body that has been driven at just about its highest speed constantly for sixty years!

I do enjoy laying off for a little while when some people come by! Ignace Paderewski stayed with me several times and his fine, sensitive nature and his breadth of experience gave him a background for a pleasant — a delightful friendship with me. He was never on his guard nor being shown off when he was here, and he felt it and appreciated it. He played, too, though not in his concert style — plainly and simply, little old-fashioned songs and pieces he knew I would understand and enjoy, and never too much, but usually too little. Schumann-Heink, that great-hearted German woman, who loved all the children of the world as she loved her own, was my guest, the great Melba came my way, and a dozen others whose names are written on my heart in gratitude to them for their interest and friendliness.

Thomas Edison I met in Sacramento when he came to California to visit the Pan-American Exposition. I had been invited to go to Sacramento to meet him; he and Henry Ford were traveling in the same party, and it was a great conclave for me. Just a little while ago I had a letter from a man who saw that meeting; it is more expressive than anything I can write of it, so I am going to quote from Bob Lyle's letter. He wrote:

I don't think you know when it was I first saw you. I was working for the railroad at Sacramento, and I heard that Edison and a party were coming through and would stop over for a while.

When I went out to see the sights some one told me Luther Burbank was coming, too, to meet Edison's party and Henry Ford, so I went back to the despatcher and I said: 'You'd better step out here a minute, because you are going to see something you will never see in your life again — the three biggest men in America, all at once.' He was very busy, but he went with me and we stayed for twenty minutes.

I saw you meet Edison and he put an arm around you, then you met Ford. You had a little talk, then Ford talked to Mr. Edison. Every once in a while Edison would lean over to his wife, because he was very deaf, you remember, and he would holler out: 'What did he say, mother?' Then she would tell him and he would laugh and then you would all have a good laugh.

It was certainly a treat for the railroad boys and the crowd, and I remember thinking then that the big men were the simplest and plainest and pleasantest, if you could see them actually in the flesh; there was no buncombe or show or pretense, but just three fellows glad to meet and having a nice time about it. I will never forget it, and I guess none of us will that saw you. Pretty soon the conductor signalled and you all went off together, and the last thing I saw you and Edison were arm in arm in the car talking away, with Edison bending down and holding his hand to his ear to make out what you had to say, and anxious not to miss a word.

Edison and Ford and their party came out to the Santa Rosa gardens a few days later and we had a grand reunion. They wanted to know everything about the flowers and the plans and the programme, and Edison was particularly quick to see beauty and catch the vision of what was being done and attempted. Henry Ford was just as enthusiastic, but he saw a different angle of the gardens. He wanted to know what was being done to increase production and develop new possibilities in plants; he is as keen as mustard and has the longest view into the future of any man I have encountered out of the business world of my time. The ladies said we acted like three schoolboys, but we didn't care. We were having a boss time!

Dr. David Starr Jordan and Hugo de Vries were the most interesting scientists I have encountered in a long experience with that class, though there have been others that I enjoyed enormously, many of them foreigners, with difficult English or none at all, and yet whom I could understand and who understood me because, with our botanical names for things and with signs and a common interest and concern, we were able to walk through the gardens and talk Nature's language without the slightest difficulty. My plants went to all parts of the world with these visitors, and my notions of method and technique were given wide dissemination through them. At the same time I learned from all of them and was helped by all of them and found friends and collaborators in all of them.

Dear John Burroughs was an intimate and crony of mine long before we met or exchanged a line of writing; I looked forward to his visit, when the time came, with the keenest pleasure and delight, and I was not disappointed. We just chinned and chinned and romanced and laughed and exaggerated to each other by the hour, and when he went away I promised to name a strawberry for him. But a long time afterward I wrote him that though I had produced a quantity of fine strawberries I never found one I thought sufficiently admirable and incomparable to send into the world with his honored name. Then, before I was satisfied, he died, and I lost a friend and the world lost one of its richest treasures. I am still hoping to find a fruit or a flower I think worthy of that name of his, and if I do I will honor myself more than him in borrowing the use of it.

John Muir and Jack London were neighbors of mine, in a sense; Muir lived outside Oakland and the great story-teller just over the hills in The Valley of the Moon. We did not bother each other — we three — but we visited now and again. Muir was a sturdy, powerful oak of a man, with a broad view of life and a marvelous sympathy; Jack London was a big healthy boy with a taste for serious things, but never cynical, never bitter, always good-humored and humorous, as I saw him, and with fingers and heart equally sensitive when he was in my gardens.

It was a long time ago that I discovered that newspaper men and press agents were fond of using me as a stalking horse to get space for pet enterprises or individuals of their own, and once or twice I had to shut down pretty smartly on this sort of exploitation. But when it was all part of the game of life I didn't mind so much; I suppose it is to publicity promoters that I owe many of the visits I have had from celebrities in their own fields who would not likely have visited an old crank like me from choice. But when they come we usually get along famously: there have been a number of motion-picture stars and a crowd of athletes and young folks famous in sports and better known to the average American than any vice-president who ever presided over the Senate! I have found them healthy, clean-minded, likable youngsters; I don't know of any finer influence on our life than the influence of play, and as long as it is indulged for the sake of the sport and the healthy rivalry and the fun there is in it, any good player is a credit to game and public alike. It's too bad they fall into the hands of the money-makers, but they do and probably always will. They don't last long there, though; soon they lose their drawing power at the gate and their promoters and managers and fair-weather friends drop away and they sink back into oblivion and are forgotten where the names of men and women who have played for the team or the college or the society or the city just for fun and for pride and pleasures are written in gold on the hearts of those they have represented and who will never forget them or their prowess!

When I ponder the roll of those who have been here, I am filled with happy memories and each name recalls some characteristic or anecdote or friendly tilt that warms my heart. Dr. O. F. Cook, of the Department of Agriculture, with his keen, incisive mind; Dr. William Rainey Harper, first president of Chicago University, who was so quiet, seldom speaking, but listening with the liveliest appreciation and suddenly putting in a word or a phrase that showed he was half a mile ahead of the rest of us; Svante Arrhenius, the Swedish physicist, ever on the alert for the causes and tendencies of things, whether they were atoms, plants, or planets; J. W. Osterhout, who was then with the University of California and later went to Yale, one of the best-equipped men I ever knew on the subject of behavior in the plant world.

But they were not all scholars — these men I remember so kindly. W. C. Edes, the civil engineer, had moved mountains and built lakes — when I saw him last he was about to span Alaska with a railroad, and no living man was better equipped to tackle that job. Jacob Riis, friend and associate of Theodore Roosevelt, was *my* friend and associate as soon as we got on the subject of children, for whom he did so much. James Bryce, the eminent historian and England's most famous ambassador to Washington, was perhaps as well-posted a man as ever came my way; but I think I derived my keenest pleasure from listening to the smooth, suave, pungent English of Elbert Hubbard, who could say such old things in such a new way as to make a person sit up straight! And in more recent years I enjoyed a warm friendship with Henry T. Finck, the New York musical critic who turned garden expert and wrote a delightful and valuable book on the subject.

Famous and illustrious women have come, too — authors, musicians, actresses, educators, and have been welcome because they were charming and interesting and because, perhaps more than most men, they have a keen natural love for flowers. Annie Laurie, the newspaper woman; Ella Wheeler Wilcox, the poetess; Carrie Jacobs Bond, the song-writer; Corra Harris, Alice Hubbard, and scores more have come to my doorbell and made me happier and better from having a few minutes' chat with them.

Of all these the one I am least likely to forget has been a recent caller. For years I had been interested in the amazing struggle against an apparently insurmountable physical disability made by Helen Keller, and you may be sure that I welcomed her to my home and gardens when she came, just a few months ago, with the greatest joy. We were instantly friends. We understood one another and I saw through her fingers as much as she saw through my eyes.

I have taken a few random pictures from the album of my memory of visitors who have come to me and walked with me in my gardens. They have inspired me, helped me, strengthened me when I was discouraged, appreciated my work more than it deserved; they have been to me what friends are always and everywhere — the most beautiful gift of life to us, at once the easiest to win and the most costly to lose!

XVII

THE NEW CREATIONS bulletins of 1893 to 1901 brought me to the peak of my activities. In eight years I disposed of no less than seven hundred different varieties of flowers, trees, shrubs, vines, and grains, and I had enough newspaper notice to have satisfied Barnum. Meantime I had started working on cactus with the aim of removing the spines from the plant and improving its size and nutritive qualities, having long been interested in the idea of producing something that would be useful and profitable for our great southwestern deserts. This was one of my most interesting projects, and one from which, I am now confident, the world will some day reap an unbelievable benefit.

The most elaborate, the most expensive, the most painful and physically difficult, and the most interesting single series of experiments I ever made I made with the cactus. There were, to begin with, over a thousand known varieties of this plant listed, and it was necessary for me to obtain specimens of as many of these varieties as possible. Before I was through I had received, planted, and studied more than six hundred of the total number, and my farms carried the largest single collection in the world. As to cost, I paid collectors thousands of dollars for their labors in gathering the specimens and in transportation expenses in getting them to Santa Rosa. In addition I spent more than sixteen years at this work, and kept a sizable force of men at work off and on all the time assisting me. So it was expensive.

As to the painful and exhausting nature of the experiment series, I can only say that I would not go through it again for all the rewards man can give! Knowing well the painful and, in some cases, the dangerous nature of the spines of the cactus I began by exercising the most scrupulous care in handling the plants. But presently it was clear that kid-glove methods in a venture that forced me to handle as high as six thousand cactus slabs in one day would prevent any progress being made, so I gritted my teeth and shut my eyes and went into the battle. I emerged scarred, pitted, and as full of spines as a pin-cushion. I have no doubt that my skin has been pierced or entered by a million cactus needles; at times I had so many on my hands and face that it was necessary to shave them off with a razor or to sandpaper them down so that, as they worked into the skin, as they do, there would not be enough to each individual spine to cause more than a temporary irritation. This was only one phase of the physical difficulties encountered in the experiment; the cactus slabs are heavy to handle, they grow to enormous size and some of them to a considerable height, and I had literally hundreds of thousands of them to deal with, as time passed. So that the mere manual labor involved was tremendous.

But, aside from the reward of having produced a new and valuable plant to add to man's store, I was well repaid by the cactus in the interest its life-history and its development during the work had for me, absorbed as I have always been in the mir-

acles and marvels of Nature. Every step of the long
series of experiments was full of delight for the
naturalist, but more than anything else I was
gratified to be able to prove, through this series, two
of the fundamental laws that I maintain underlie all
biology.

The pliability of life — the capacity it has for
varying so that successive generations acquire new
characteristics, new possibilities and powers and new
advantages, and the capacity for adding these new
things to the heredity so that definite improvement
is continuous — was one of the first fundamentals I
discovered through my early work with plants, and
on it I based my experiments. I had proved it time
and again to my own satisfaction, but the cactus
gave me a demonstration that there could be no
possible question about. It is so important a law,
and so significant to man that I want to tell the life-
story of the cactus briefly to make the point clear.

While varieties of the cactus family are widely
scattered through those territories of earth where
the climate is hot and dry, the greatest assortment
and the most numerous growths are found throughout the Southwest and in northern Mexico. What
we call the southwestern deserts were once ocean-
bed. Constructional and sedimentary changes occurred that surrounded great arms of the sea and
cut off the sea-water from the parent bodies, form-
ing inland salt lakes. Evaporation was greater than
rainfall and the lakes began to diminish.

As dry land appeared, plant growth found footing;
among other growths were the progenitors of the
cactus we know. But they were entirely different in

nature and characteristics — instead of great, pulpy slabs they grew small leaves from slender stems, they were smooth and harmless, and they developed small, bright-colored flowers, and bore small, probably acid fruits. They were attractive to insects and animals, because the cactus plant needed to advertise to insure the dissemination of its seeds. Due to the presence still of large bodies of water the climate was moist and warm, and the cactus flourished.

But as evaporation continued to decrease the size of the inland seas, and finally to dissipate them altogether, the climate changed, the heat became more intense, rains grew less frequent and less generous, native plants that could not adapt themselves rapidly enough or that did not have in their heredity the stamina to withstand the rigor of the new climate were crowded out by the sturdy cactus, the sagebrush, the greasewood, the mesquite, the salt-weed, and so on, and gradually disappeared. Now began an era of terrible trial for the plants. The change to desert, once started, was comparatively rapid — that is, instead of completely altering its nature in fifty thousand years these southwestern sea-beds may have been transformed into desert in a few hundred. It was speedy traveling for plants, and only the most adaptable could keep up the pace.

Not only this, but the death of other vegetation in those regions left the surviving varieties prey to all the herbivorous animals which ranged there; in self-defense the sage became bitter, the salt-weed dry and unpleasant, the mesquite like iron, and so on. The cactus, succulent, growing larger leaves as it needed to store more and more moisture, and full of sugar accumulated to carry it through hard periods of heat and the well-known bitter cold of desert Januarys, became more tempting to animals instead of less. Probably they were stripped of their leaves so often and over so long a period that they ceased to produce leaves almost altogether and grew more and more to slabs. They were robbed of their fruits, gnawed at, wounded, cut off at the base, and generally so hardly treated that they were threatened with extermination.

Finally there is no doubt that a few of them, struggling to put out new leaves from a bleeding stump, level with the ground, grew on that stump a small slab that carried hairs or protuberances and these hairs, in generations and generations, became stiffer and harder until they were spines; the spines grew more and more hard, sharp, tough, and plentiful. This protective armor was not developed in a hundred days or a hundred years or a thousand, but it *was* developed, definitely, for a definite purpose and with definite success, in the end, and became so modified and adapted to the purpose for which it was brought into being that the time came when a buffalo or an antelope or a rabbit could get exactly as much satisfaction out of a porcupine or a two-thousand-volt electric wire!

Now, how do I know that this development of the cactus spines was the result of a definite need and built up by the slow acquisition, generation after generation, of new and vital and slowly acquired characteristics? I know it, and no logical mind could deny it, but how can I prove it to the satisfaction of science, which takes nothing for granted?

I will give you my proof.

Innumerable cactus plants exist that have no spines whatever and are as tender and succulent and attractive to animals as the desert plants, but these harmless varieties and individuals are always found growing in crevices or cracks or caves or inaccessible places where no herbivorous animal could possibly reach them!

And I will give you another proof.

In sixteen years, by crossing cactus with few spines on cactus having spines, but possessed of desirable qualities such as great size, rapid growth, extreme succulence of leaves, and so on, I have carried the cactus back to the day when it had no spines because it needed none, and have perfected a spineless cactus in a length of time that, compared with the period which saw the change from smooth cactus to the vicious, armored variety, is but a moment.

And incidentally I want to add a remarkable fact that is both interesting and instructive in this connection. My spineless cactus slabs, when very young and tender, have growths on them that are plainly vestigial leaves — that is, structures with all the qualities and characteristics of leaves, as in the original cactus of prehistoric times, but that slough off soon because the leaf-bearing habit is not now more than dimly in the heredity of the plant. These vestigial reminders or remains of real leaves could be developed, by selection and proper cultivation, back into actual leaves, so that the cactus could be made to complete its round-trip from its first condition through its condition of an armored desert plant and back to its first form once more! There is something more you will not find in the textbooks, and it knocks a lot of so-called scientific theories into a cocked hat!

The other fundamental I have demonstrated conclusively with the cactus is more original with me and more important to my work. Because it was not necessary for me to prove that heredity is the sum of all environments — I know it from the beginning, since I first read it in Darwin, who believed it from the first to the end of his remarkable life, and it was just as much a fact to me as that plant life takes its force from the sun and that all other life owes its existence to plants, if you look far enough! I did need to demonstrate and prove the second theory, because my success was contingent on it, and without it I should have stopped as an ordinary seedsman or nurseryman and been known now only as 'the Santa Rosa nurseryman with the place south of the iron bridge.'

This second fundamental law is that adaptability —the power to vary to its own advantage in a plant, just as in a worm or a wolf or a man — depends on its history — its heredity — and is greater as vicissitudes and perils and struggles have been greater in its past.

Two young men come to you asking for work. One is the son of a well-to-do family that, for a dozen generations, have found life easy and tranquil and more or less pleasant. The other is the son of a man who was himself buffeted, pressed, driven, persecuted by ill fortune and care and privation, and whose fathers before him never had a chance, but always had to struggle and sweat and toil to gain a bare livelihood. Granted that both families have been equally industrious, honest, and ambitious, which of those two boys would you engage?

Probably the first. But I want to tell you that ninety-nine times in every hundred the second boy would be just exactly as much better as a risk for you as his stamina, determination, ambition, and quality is better because of the refining and hardening process undergone by his forefathers. In America we are often amazed at the incapacity and indolence and repeated failures of the sons of our 'best families,' and equally astonished at the rapid rise of young immigrant boys or the children of families reared in the slums of New York. We have a proverb in New England to the effect that 'from shirt-sleeves to shirt-sleeves is three generations' — that the children of the men whose fathers sweated to gain wealth and who themselves have spent their lives dissipating those hard-earned fortunes will have to return to shirt-sleeves before they die. What is behind the proverb? A vague recognition of the law that it takes many generations to produce the fiber that can make and stand success.

You believe, perhaps, that you can think of cases that disprove this. Very well. Take two of the best-known New York families, without naming names. One earned the money by hard and difficult and untiring labor, and the sons and daughters inherited the desire to go on working hard. That family is clean, free from taint, industrious, and highly successful. But the other family I have in mind merely inherited wealth that came from the great multiplying of real estate values, and its children for two or three generations have been wasters, prodigals, notorious, and gradually losing everything in life except what can be bought and paid for in hard cash!

On the other hand, take the converse of the proposition and consider two other cases. Here is a boy whose father came of a long line of hard-working and very poor Dutch farmers and laborers. They knew nothing through a dozen generations but hardship, work, and privation. When the boy came to this country at twelve years of age or such a matter, he set out to seize the opportunities that opened before his amazed eyes at every turn. He educated himself, worked, learned, kept himself decent, adapted himself to his new environment, and began to go ahead. The sterling qualities that had been impressed on him by repetition, repetition, repetition, of trial and difficulty and poverty, through many generations of Dutchmen, suddenly emerged in him, and he became one of the three or four greatest editors and most successful Americans of our times. Opposed to him take the sons of the poor white trash of the southern mountains. Almost without exception there has been no improvement there in five generations, but on the contrary there has been a steady retrogression. Why? Because hardship and poverty have been accepted as inevitable, the men of those families have surrendered to life, their women have been discouraged, lazy, slovenly, and worthless from birth, and repetition, repetition, repetition has impressed on their children sloth, cowardice, unfitness, disease, and degradation.

In my work it was necessary for me to take advantage of every favorable fact and condition I could find. It was a long time before I woke to the fact that the heredity of a plant — its life-story — was just as important to me before I began to attempt a development of it as a clinical history of a new patient is necessary to a physician who wants to make a useful diagnosis. When I did, it was this law that I discovered. The plant with the greatest variability was the one with which I could do the most, with the least effort, and with the greatest chance of success. The plant that had lived along for generation after generation without any trouble or stress or hardship or change in its condition and environment was as set in its way as a grindstone and as stubborn as a mule!

The cactus presented to me the most perfect possible example of the indubitable truth of this law. Take the rose, for contrast. For a thousand years, probably, men have trained and cultivated rosebushes, giving them care, good soil, plenty of water and tending — the most favorable spots in the garden and the most jealous watching to protect them from enemies of every kind. The result is that the rose must have that sort of care continued or it will die as sure as moonrise! The nearer the rose is to the wild state the hardier it is; the more refined and high-bred and aristocratic, the more you have to sit up nights with it and give it a flannel overcoat and keep the aphis out of its hair. It has been bred to have nursing and attention, and so it simply lies down and quits if it does not receive it.

Take a cactus slab — born of generations — thousands of generations! — of scorching heat, the attacks of enemies, the buffeting of winds, the parching, searing drought of summer and the bitter, piercing cold of a desert winter. Throw that slab on the ground. From the eyes on the under-side will grow roots. From the eyes exposed to the sun will grow new slabs. How can that be? There is not a particle of difference between the eyes above and those below. What taught the cactus to seize at life in this fashion, adjusting itself to apparently impossible circumstances and doing the right thing at the right time and in the right direction? Heredity! The lessons its fathers learned, through bitter and almost fatal experiences through ten thousand years of struggle for life. Throw a rose cutting on the ground and it will curl up and die like a fish out of water!

Put a slab of cactus away in a dark cellar. Almost anything else in the vegetable world would give up in a few days. Leave the cactus there for eight months or a year and then look at it, and you will find that it has put out two or three or half a dozen feeble, pale, sickly slabs, or leaves, and is alive and kicking, and will simply jump ahead if you plant it in the poorest corner of your garden! I hung a cactus plant in a tree, head down, for four years once, and when I planted it, it started to grow within ten days. I laid a slab on a shelf that was covered with burlap and that was four feet from the ground, and presently I discovered that the cactus was develop-

ing new slabs and that its roots had gone through
the burlap and were feeling their way along the
cracks of the adjacent wall, reaching for that earth
that was so far below it!

You know, you can't have sixteen years' acquaintance with a plant like that, and get to know its personal history and intimate details of its life, without
conceiving a certain admiration for it even while
you are engaged with a magnifying glass and a pair
of forceps in trying to extract from your hand eighty
or ninety piercing needles that the same plant has
given you as a birthday present!

It has been said that my spineless cactus varieties are not a practical benefit to mankind, but I
just let that sort of talk go in one ear and out the
other. When I remember that in my own boyhood
tomatoes were a forbidden fruit because they were
considered poisonous; when I recall the difficulty I
had in introducing some of my earliest plums to
growers who have since reaped thousands and thousands of dollars from them and have grown them so
long that most of them have forgotten whence they
came; when I think of the bungling methods used in
trying to produce valuable and splendid new varieties of every kind and sort of plant, and the mistakes that are made by farmers and orchardists and
gardeners until experience teaches them how the
new things should be utilized; and finally when I
consider that very few men understand that the
plant developer is only the producer of the new invention and cannot go out into the world and experiment with it to find where it is most remunera-
tive, what uses of it are the most profitable, and

what treatments of it are necessary to make it most valuable to mankind, I do not worry about the spineless cactus.

It will grow with a minimum of care and cultivation on hundreds of thousands of acres now sterile; it is more than ninety per cent water, sugar, and highly valuable mineral elements, it will produce from one hundred and fifty to three hundred tons of forage to the acre and, at the end of five or six years, one third as much fruit, which is nutritive and delicious; and it will multiply by division — that is, grow from slabs — indefinitely and with incredible rapidity.

Once it has a start — jack-rabbits alone can keep a new field of cactus cut off clean to the ground if they are given the run of the place! — nothing can kill it. A plant like that needs no advertising and no apologies! I may add that I have not a single slab of it for sale and have not had for a good many years. I am not writing a prospectus for it; I am trying to tell you what an amazing experiment it has proved and how generously and richly it has repaid me in sound knowledge and infinite interest, aside from every other consideration.

The spineless cactus project, from first to last, was a big, bold one, from which I learned more than from any other one experiment, and that time will prove the value of to the world. If my contention is correct that this cactus of mine will thrive in arid and semi-arid regions and provide food for cattle, it will revolutionize our stock problem, make thousands wealthy and tens of thousands independent, and will re-create our deserts. If it is correct, there could not be a better illustration of the possibilities inherent in plant breeding.

This has been my text for thirty or forty years — the need of more work with the plants on which the wealth of our planet is built. Not only have I preached it in season and out, but I have never begrudged the time necessary to the delivery of the sermon whenever I could get a congregation. I have always freely described my methods, principally because I wanted others to learn about the work, become interested in it, and ground themselves in its fundamentals so that they could proceed with it. Other fields seem more attractive; there are many other lines that are more sensational and showy.

But here is a world almost untouched by trained and enthusiastic experts; it is not Burbank's work, nor is Burbank unique in it. I have gone farther than any one else, and operated on a larger scale, and accomplished something in more different branches of plant breeding, but, as has been often repeated in these pages, I have only skimmed the surface of possibilities; with me and after me must come, not two or three, but hundreds of young men and women eager, industrious, patient, far-seeing, humble, to explore the field, map out its riches, and then develop them for the good of all mankind.

XVIII

READING biography, especially of men whose primary object has been something other than money-making, I have noticed that most of them sooner or later run into a promoter or a promotion and get badly singed. I have been no exception, though I must say that I do not believe any of the men who tried to exploit or subsidize me or my work had base motives. On the contrary, most of them were actuated by a desire to increase my usefulness and to widen the scope of my experiments and to broadcast the results over a greater area. No, I could usually smell out a rascal before he had reached the front door, and so could head him off.

I would rather have five energetic and competent enemies than one fool friend; now and again my friends have led me astray and it has cost me a lot of money, a world of trouble, and a multitude of worries before I got back on the main track again. For more than twenty years I was embroiled in business relations with various people, and I had my wisdom teeth cut on some pretty tough bones in that period.

The spineless cactus enterprise attracted a great deal of attention; taken altogether I had quite a name. I had delivered a lecture or two and written constantly of my own specialty; a group of friends suggested that I should give up my actual experiments and go to teaching my methods to others at one of the big universities. In spite of the fact that I was definitely opposed to this project from the

first, I was approached by several educators and
finally I did give a series of lectures as part of the
regular course at Stanford University. But I stead-
fastly refused to turn teacher; what I needed was to
be free to attend to my experiments, which were still
way up in the thousands year in and year out, and
when the universities could not get me my friends
went to work to obtain a subsidy for me so that I
could have all my thought and energy to devote to
the farms.

The result, after a good deal of activity on my behalf which was unsolicited and somewhat embarrassing to me, was that the Carnegie Institution proposed to give me a stated sum each year for expenses
and to put some of its research experts at work with
me to study my methods and record my results. I
accepted with many misgivings which were later
justified by experience. The sum paid me did not
prove sufficient to meet my monthly expenses, and
the experts sent found it difficult to get much data
except by interviewing me. This took so much time
that I had little left for experimentation — the sole
object and purpose of my life — and presently the
scheme was abandoned. I had always said, and
said then, that my job was to create and get results,
rather than record the steps and details, and since
the day held only twenty-four hours it was impossible to be an experimenter and a writer of scientific
or practical books at the same time.

This experience led, however, to the business relationships I entered on, when I did actually try to
do both. A book company was promoted which un-
dertook to publish my writings, give me a royalty,

and attend to publishing and marketing. For seven or eight years I was the busiest man on this planet; I suppose I wrote as many words as any one who ever lived, but the book people got into numerous difficulties, failed to live up to agreement, and finally went out of business, owing me almost a hundred thousand dollars.

In the meantime another outfit conceived the idea of establishing a company for distributing the products of my farms, and this 'seed company,' as we called it, became an elaborate and complicated affair with a big office building, scores of employees, a large number of fat salaries for every one but myself, and a top-heavy business that resulted in disaster. Here, too, to add to my worries and my work, the promoters found themselves in deep water because they did not understand the business of selling seeds, trees, bulbs, and cuttings, and because everything they knew had to come from me. It was too much for me, naturally. Again I was the sufferer, to the tune of a good many thousand dollars, and in the end the 'seed company' went into a receiver's hands.

These were the outstanding business experiences of my life, though there were numerous other adventures that were expensive and wearisome and even galling to me. From them I learned a good deal about men, however, and about the world of promotion, financing, share-issuing, share-selling, and share-speculation, and a great deal about my own physical limitations. The truth is that I should have kept to my own line, at which I had made a success both as a scientific plant developer and as a business man; it is certain that no one with a big creative task can lean on the crutch of a financial subsidy or a financial arrangement and still have his hands free.

If I had read Nature's book more closely I should have been warned by its lessons as well as by my own instincts in these matters. Man's institutions, man's knowledge, and man's conclusions are built imitatively from natural phenomena, derived from natural sources or drawn from natural laws. Cupidity, greed, and selfishness are about the only purely human inventions we can find — the hog's habits are due to the fact that he is hungry all the time and not to the fact that he is just plain swinish toward his fellow hogs! Outside of those three attributes of man, pretty much everything else he has comes to him direct from Nature, and there is an analogy somewhere for most of his contrivances, most of his characteristics, and most of his devices, no matter how elaborate.

Every sort and kind and variety of crutch, in Nature and in man, is harmful except the prop that is made necessary by an actual physical deformity. In Nature the weaklings fall out of the race, and the plants or animals that cannot do their work and make their way unaided are dispensed with pretty summarily. Man attempts to support and strengthen himself with various aids and assistances, but it is rarely ever that his plan succeeds. The man or the institution that is really necessary and really efficient does not need an endowment. By that I do not mean that such organizations as universities should be strictly self-supporting. The fact is that educa-

tion, where it is free, as in this country, is the job of
the State — of Society, because the immediate returns from education go to the individual and not to
the institution. Therefore either the public as a po-
litical entity has to supply the necessary funds or
else the public as a group of voluntary donors has to
do it.

But the fundamental law is there: crutches are for
cripples, and they are weakening and debasing to a
healthy, normal man. The help and comfort and
impetus we get from appreciation and praise is useful and fine to the best of us, but when it is leaned
on and when it causes us to relax our own efforts or
ambition or push, it becomes a crutch — and a
feeble and wobbly crutch at that, that will let us
down with a bump if we put much weight on it.

There is an excellent reason for this, which can be
found repeated and repeated in illustrations from
Nature. The individual must be self-reliant and, in
a sense, self-sufficient, or else he goes down. By
self-sufficient I mean able to employ his own efforts
and capitalize his own abilities so that they coördi-
nate with the efforts and abilities of others without
putting any weight on them. Biologists call this
symbiosis — the mutual help results from an inter-
change of activities between two separate individuals or organisms. It is interestingly and vividly illustrated in the relation between the bee and the flower.

Without the bee the flower could not, in many
cases, pollinize even its own stigma, and certainly
could not pollinize the stigmas of other flowers.
Without the flower the bee could not live five minutes. The blossom, therefore, long ago learned to

construct itself so that, somewhere below its reproductive organs, was a little pantry of sweets. Seeking that larder, the bee brushed against the pollen-
laden stamen and not only scattered the precious
grains about the place, but carried some of them
with him to the next flower. Neither the bee nor
the flower is a crutch; they are mutually helpful and
mutually dependent.

Illustrations of that phenomenon can be found all
through Nature; except for parasites all Nature's
children help one another, but all are self-sufficient,
too, and if they are not they fall by the wayside.
Human beings practice symbiosis in almost every relation they have with one another; they have added
the refinement of wanting something for nothing,
and sometimes they succeed in getting it. But not
often, without paying a heavy price either in public
esteem or in humiliation or degradation or a weakening process of some sort. And the man or the organization that seeks to get some one else to do the
work laid out to be done is absolutely certain to
weaken himself, hamper others, slow up the race,
and generally make a mess of his un-Natural procedure.

Self-reliance and self-respect are about as valuable
commodities as we can carry in our pack through
life; the one depends on the other and follows it, and
you will have to search a long way through Nature
to find an instance where the individual relies wholly
on another, and merely sponges his way. The parasite happens to grow through borrowing from a tree
or a plant, but it has to find a place to take root, it
must spread leaves and extend root-mouths, and re-

sist enemies just as any other plant does. I do not present the parasite in plants as a model or pattern, but it has to be self-reliant and attend to its own job or else it cannot live. The human parasite, as found in many forms and in many grades of society, scarcely does this. He is just an encumbrance and a load on his fellows; perhaps some day we will take a lesson from the bees and kill off our drones.

The necessity for self-reliance and effort and ambition in the human individual is necessitated by the law. This law develops what is often called a struggle, and many people speak of the Darwinian theory of the survival of the fittest as harsh, cruel, and merciless. Just at present America is full of young gentlemen who are trying in art and literature and the theater to picture that struggle in its darker aspects. They call themselves realists, I believe, and the public gets the idea from them that there is only one side to the picture. That is the way with us: we have a sluggish liver or we overeat or we wake up with a headache and all day long we can only see the dark side of things. We deplore the fight we have to make for existence, for happiness, for decency and uprightness; it looks so much easier to give up and be immoral and lazy and blame natural law for the whole business!

But the struggle for existence is what makes the world what it is, both the dark side and the light and beautiful and inspiring. It was a struggle for existence that caused flowerless and dull plants to put out their advertising matter, in the form of entrancing blossoms, thus attracting bees and birds and bringing about the fertilization necessary to their continued life. It was the same struggle that brought perfume into the world; it was the war of forces that gashed the earth with such wonders as the Grand Canyon of the Colorado, that broke open the rocks that form the magic glory of Yosemite, that created Niagara Falls, the Adirondacks, and that gave us the illimitable ocean washing the shores of our continents.

It was the struggle for existence that sent the elm, the walnut, and the redwood towering into space; that lays a blanket of white on the earth in winter and follows it with the effulgent beauty of early spring, leaping into renewed life in fairy robes of green, set with the gems of little flowers. It was the struggle for existence that gave us our farms, our cities, our steamships, our railroads, our factories, turning out necessities, comforts, and luxuries every day until life is becoming easier and sweeter for every human on this planet. It was the struggle for existence that gave us Mahomet and Christ and Charlemagne and Napoleon and Lincoln and Rockefeller and Edison, and all our pioneers and leaders and warriors and thinkers and doers in a world that is not made up entirely of failures and traitors and rascals, in spite of the gloomy writers and the liverish painters and the dyspeptic playwrights!

It is the struggle for existence, so-called, that gives us all our beauty and sweetness and pleasure and health and love and happiness — our little children, our dogs and birds, our poetry and romance and song, too. Because in the heredity of the race is a great questing and need and urge for beauty; that urge accumulates and accumulates, gen-

eration after generation, in a family of plain and un-
distinguished history, until finally it bursts forth
in a Beethoven, a Keats, or a Whitman, in a Whis-
tler, or Abbey, in a Saint-Gaudens or a Christopher
Wren. The need for beauty is as positive a natural
impulse as the need for food, though it is a later
development and therefore not so deep-rooted and
so all-absorbing; nevertheless you know there are
people everywhere who will go without several
meals to attend a musical programme or will sacrifice clothing to buy a picture. This æsthetic side of
man, as in all Nature, is one of the last refinements
added to the list, but because it is a younger appetite or need does not mean that it is not an important and even vital one.

The struggle for existence is not actually a struggle at all. You cannot sit beside the ocean and
watch the breakers pounding, pounding, pounding
at the cliffs, dashing their great weight at the rock,
throwing rainbow-tinted veils of spray high in air,
and roaring into caverns and booming around reefs
without being awed and impressed by the tremendous beauty of the scene. You cannot stand in a
garden and contemplate the butterflies and the
hummingbirds and the bees sailing or whirring or
darting from one lovely blossom to another without
being rested and refreshed and gratified. Yet in
both cases this impulse that is so wrongly called 'the
struggle for existence' is being perfectly exemplified
before your eyes!

Is not the sea striving to batter down the cliffs
and pulverize the rocks to sand and eat into the land
to carry it away to fill its bottomless bed? Is not the

butterfly hurrying to get its sip of sweet before death overtakes it and leaves it no time to mature and deposit the egg which will bring about a caterpillar that will turn into another butterfly? Is not the bee storing food for the hive to make possible the life of the swarm that is to come? Is not the hummingbird whirring through its work, hardpressed to get a store of food for its little ones, tucked away in a tiny hammock-nest somewhere under a palm leaf or in a thicket of hedge? It is life or death for the sea and the land. Which will win? It is life or death for flower and bird and insect. But that is the hard and cruel and merciless and untrue picture of the business.

What is really going on all about us is a play of two forces. Is the law of gravity cruel and relentless? Is it a pity that that shooting star goes flaming through the heavens to disappear into space? Is the hunger of the baby or the absorption of the poet to put his thought into rhyme piteous? Is it a hard law that water quenches your thirst, that fire warms you, that food gives you strength, that electricity pulses in the lamp globe and turns the filament white-hot to light your book as you sit reading this? And yet in all those you see two forces playing on and in and through Life. Call it positive and negative, call it attraction and repulsion, call it movement and rest — call it what you will; but by whatever name it goes it is two opposites acting and interacting and counteracting and reacting one on the other through the whole universe, and by its processes and procedures bringing into our existence pleasure and pain, hunger and food, thirst and water, heat and cold, joy and sorrow, success and failure, black and white, light and shadow, tears and laughter — the flaming star and the midnight blackness of a cave, a beautiful woman and a crawling slug, a cruel tyrant and a laughing baby, a redwood tree and the poison ivy, the abundant health of the athlete and the running and putrid sores of a leper!

Those who prefer see only the blackness, the slug, the monster, poisonous air, and deadly disease. For me I like to walk in my gardens and see this eternal interplay of the two forces as it appears in beauty and fragrance; I prefer the glad welcome in the eyes of my dog, Bonita, and the glad shout of delight from my little ward, Betty Jane; I choose to contemplate the serenity of my home, the companionship of my dear wife, my Betty, the staunch loyalty of my friends, the warming and almost universal gratitude of the people of the world to me for the work I have done and the service I am trying to perform.

No; the struggle for existence, and the difficulties into which a few business relationships brought me, and the failure of trusted men, and the pettiness of a few, and the handicaps and weaknesses and debilities that have hampered me are negligible to me. At seventy-seven years of age I can look back with pleasure and delight on my experience. To me the struggle has been a game, free from bitterness, broken only by just penalties, played with the utmost fairness under the rules, and leaving me now the sense of having won a few points and made a few first places and having been rewarded generously for my effort. The law of life, Darwin said, is the survival of the fittest; I would like to amend his statement and assert that the law is the boundless reward of the industrious, the courageous, the true — in short, of *the fit!*

XIX

WE are so accustomed to the use of figurative language in sermons, essays, and stories nowadays that it is sometimes difficult to make people understand that true science does not employ metaphors and similes, unless by way of emphasis or for the sake of clearness, but means what it says. That is one reason why science has a language all its own and why it has to invent new words to describe new factors or formulas or discoveries in the onward march of knowledge.

It is important for the reader to understand that, except to make my point clear or by way of the emphasis of fable, I have been writing in literal terms in these chapters. For instance, the repeated assertion I have made that Nature's laws are universally true and applicable is meant to be taken exactly as it is set down — there is no parable intended when I have said again and again that the same fundamental laws apply to the crystal and the star, the egg and the fruit, the birdlet and the seedling, the man and the elephant. And this common law of Nature results in a very exact parallel between the life of the plant which has absorbed me for almost seventy years, and the life of the world's greatest treasure, asset, and hope — the child.

In a little book I published a few years ago I went into this subject at some length; since that time I have been increasingly impressed with the analogy between plant breeding and the breeding, rearing, training, and education of children. I am more and more convinced, too, that the underlying principles of my work have a definite significance in this connection, and I could not round out this harvest of my years without summing up my experience and conclusions, feeling as strongly as I do that the simplicity of the principles and their enormous importance alike commend them to the thoughtful parent or teacher — to all, in fact, who are interested in children.

This subject is one to which great attention has already been given, but you will observe generally that the authorities are specialists in some phase of medical knowledge, of education, of pedagogy, of psychology, or of physical training, and very few of them have succeeded, in my opinion, in withdrawing from their professional points of view and taking a wide and impersonal look at the whole field. Certainly almost none of them have been naturalists, which appears to me to be the first thing every sound trainer or teacher of children should be!

If you wanted to break a horse you could find books on the science of the veterinary, on horse breeding, on horse racing, on saddles and bridles, and on the nutritive value of various feeds, but you would have to read them all, and a lot more, if you were going to understand the horse sufficiently well to make him obedient, docile, useful, and a friend. If you were expecting to assume the responsibilities of parenthood and wanted to be competent to carry the job through in a workmanlike fashion, you would find yourself confronted with a whole library of books on pre-natal care of the mother and child,

on obstetrics, on feeding, on bathing, on early training, on physical education, on psychology, and so on
through the whole list, and yet with a year's reading I doubt seriously that you would find more than
a scant reference to the fundamentals of life on
which all that is true in your books must be based
and without which every pretty theory and fanciful
conceit and table of statistics is mostly guesswork
and largely misleading!

What I have been trying to say in these chapters
is that those fundamentals are amazingly simple and
plain to understand, and that any one who learns
them and correlates them with the other facts of life
and with his experience, as he goes along, can use
them in everyday life. Because I love children and
wish for every one of them a future bright and assured, and because the fundamentals of which I
write are so understandable and valuable in all your
activities, I want to set the principles down again
and then elaborate on them a little as I find them
refer to the breeding and rearing of our boys and girls.

First, then, all we know of life certainly is that it
began with the cell that, by division, reproduced itself, giving the infant cell its own character and powers and also giving it the added power of varying
so that it could adapt itself to a new environment.
The infant cell matured, added a mite or mote of
new character to what its parent had possessed, divided, and thus established a new individual that,
in turn, added a faint touch of new power or new
possibility or new nature to itself and passed this,
with the characteristics of its parent and of its
parent's parent, on to a fourth generation.

Second, the diversification of life proceeded slowly and steadily from this repeated division and this repeated addition of new characteristics to the original powers and characteristics of the first cell. Colonies of cells were formed and became the nucleus of vegetable life — the beginnings of vines and flowers and trees and vegetables, each generation adding something, if it survived under the play of negative and positive forces — hardship, drought, water too salt for it or land too moist, and so on — to the possessions of the generations that had preceded it. Vegetable growths took on the new characteristic of motive power and animal life appeared, probably first as tiny monads in warm salt water, then as the beginnings of fishes, and finally as land animals. Each generation added something because it had to add to its inherited powers and possibilities or die, and eventually the forbears of the animals we know came into being and, to be the heir to all the ages, Man at last appeared.

Third, the law of growth and development never ceased to operate, as it had from the beginning, and to-day, as much as in the dim years of æons ago, all the heredity of all that time and of all those changes comes to your newborn babe, just as there comes to it that sensitiveness to environment — to impressions from without — that was in the original infant cell, and just as there is in it the same old power to vary and to adapt itself to that environment.

Fourth, the more combinations there are in the heredity of the flower or the animal or the child of to-day, the more susceptible it is thus rendered to environmental influences and the more striking and

THE SHASTA DAISY AND MOUNT SHASTA
A favorite picture with Luther Burbank

to pick out the honest and fine man or woman from the one who is weak or silly or bad. The fact is that this is one of Nature's provisions, deeply impressed in the heredity of all life, to help the young growth to recognize its friends and shun and protect itself from its enemies. A day-old chick will cower or run for the hen's wings when a shadow is cast on it from above — the hawk-fear is bred into the chicken for a thousand generations. A very young kitten, with its eyes just opened, will arch its back and spit at a dog. A plant will lean toward the sun as soon as it is above ground, just as it will droop and try to make itself smaller the moment a storm begins. No wonder your child sees through to the innermost character of people and things about it!

It sees farther than that, too: it has an instinctive and penetrating capacity for reading motives and judging your actions, not according to their appearance, but according to what is behind them. Doesn't your own child discern almost immediately when you are lying to it? Doesn't it recognize injustice in your dealings with it? Doesn't it know just how far it can go into bullying you or cajoling you, and do you think it does not realize its advantage when you have to bribe it to obey you? A lie to a child is a thousand times more wicked than a lie to an adult, because the child not only sees through the lie, but it turns mimetically to lying as a useful and trouble-saving device. If you are unjust to your child, accuse it wrongfully, punish it unfairly, or show partiality toward a little brother or sister, you are doing a much worse act than you would be guilty of if an older person were involved. Because the child not only recognizes the wrong and suffers under it, but he stores it away for reference and employment later, and he has impressed on the sensitive plate of his brain the thought that here is another art to add to lying and deceit and the taking of bribes!

To my way of thinking, the most serious offense against the child is that of ruling it or attempting to rule or direct it through fear. I would give a longer prison sentence to a man or woman who frightens a child with the policeman, a bogy, a ghost, a big black bear, or a big black dog, than I would give a burglar, for the thief only steals that which can be replaced, but the parent or nurse who instills fear into a child takes away its most precious possessions — confidence and affection — and replaces those fine qualities with cowardice, mental and moral. I have the most complete sympathy for religion and the deepest abhorrence of which I am capable for a lying theology. Weak or ailing or frightened or ignorant women and innocent and trusting little children have always been the favorite raw material of priests; luckily the day has already dawned when love and tolerance and a desire for righteousness are being substituted for fear and dread and falsehood and mummery!

XX

DID it ever occur to you that only man-made laws prohibit?

Moses may or may not have been inspired to proclaim the Ten Commandments, but he certainly employed the human formula in more than half his rules of conduct. Jesus Christ, on the other hand, gave only two commandments and both of them were affirmative, constructive, and positive.

Nature's laws are that way — they affirm instead of prohibiting. If you violate her laws you are your own prosecuting attorney, judge, jury, and hangman; Nature says you must eat sanely, sleep soundly, care for your body, avoid anger and hatred, be industrious, sober, and self-respecting; and if you flaunt her laws you just naturally walk right into the jail of indigestion, nervous prostration, ill health, a bad heart, worthlessness, and failure; — there is no appealing the case and there is no alibi possible and no one to whom to 'pass the buck'!

In the last chapter I have drawn some conclusions from my knowledge of Nature's laws that have to do with the prohibitions in the raising of children, but that is only half the case. The precepts above cited, learned from seventy years of close application to Nature's ordinances, teach us what not to do. But there is a big and inspiring other side — the true natural laws that are affirmative and constructive. The first that comes to my mind is the law of fixing new and desirable characteristics in the little human plant through environmental influences.

In the last forty years I have proved time and again that there is not a single desirable power of which a given species of plants is capable that cannot be impressed on it by breeding, selection, and repetition, repetition, repetition. I have given scentless flowers perfume, tasteless fruits flavor, dry-colored blossoms, or those with a single hue, brilliant and variegated garments. Time after time, as already related in these pages, I have taken a definite order to produce a definite quality or set of qualities in a well-known and apparently unchangeable plant or flower or fruit and in a comparatively few generations have delivered the order. Choose any reasonable improvement you please in a plant and it can be accomplished; not only that, but it can be fixed in the plant so that, short of reversing the process employed, or permitting Nature to reverse it — 'letting the plant go back to its wild state' — it will remain fixed and unalterable in its new character.

If scientific breeding, careful selection, repetition, repetition, repetition of impressions, and tireless patience and strict adherence to the programme can achieve this in the plant world how much more surely could a definite improvement be achieved with your children, more sensitive, more adaptable, and blessed with powers of discrimination, the gift of appreciation, and the ability to reason and compare for themselves? This is not to say that you can make your boy a great financier by early training, or turn your girl into a peerless musician if she has no aptitude for music. You cannot make the peony bear wheat nor the ivy produce roses. What you can do is give the peony sturdiness, variegated color, the power to grow taller, or the habit of growing dwarfed; you can give the ivy some few new habits, within a limited range, but surely and definitely.

Why do we use as illustrations just here the peony and the ivy? Because, if I had used the plum or the poppy or the petunia I would not have been able to make so clear a parallel with the case of the growing child. The fact is that we have to take into account, in the training of the little human plant, a factor that will be found in the list of five fundamental laws enumerated above that you must get clearly into your mind in thinking of the training of your children. That factor is heredity — a variant in its power and influence, both in plant life and in all other life. Let us look at that subject a moment, from the viewpoint of naturalists and humanists — lovers of all growing things, and under the light Nature sheds on all such questions.

I have said repeatedly that the more heredities are broken up and combined or recombined the more plastic and adaptable is the resultant cross. You throw the plant out of its accustomed routine — you blow it into fragments as though with dynamite. Many of the old characteristics, traits, and tendencies on both sides are sent sky-high and never come down, but in the recombinations that do occur you catch heredity off balance — teetering and swaying — and for that reason the more ready to follow suggestions or leads given it from outside — that is, from environment. I have been the environment that was directing and leading in my plant experiments — that is just what I have been, an environmental influence, and a strong one!

I said in an earlier chapter that the reason I could work so successfully with the California poppy was because I found it a plant with an unbalanced and teetering heredity because of its comparative youth and because it had had to adjust itself to widely different environments in order to live in the widely diversified climates and soils of its native state. So it was amenable to suggestions and responded to the push and the urge I gave it. But I should have hesitated a long time before beginning experiments with the oak or the palm or the ivy, or even the peony. Why? Because back of the oak trees, the palms (especially of the California and other deserts) and the ivy vine are heredities stretching down the centuries into an unknown dawn of time, unchanging, unchanged, and perhaps almost unchangeable. True, the oak has developed into a considerable number of varieties, and there are many kinds of palms and a few of ivy. But generally speaking these variations have been but slight — so slight that you will find only a few people who can unfailingly distinguish between the varieties and name them all and describe their differences exactly. The main heredity line is a strong, definite chain, and the essential characteristics shown by all the links are so fixed that it would require a charge of T.N.T. to break them up — mere gunpowder wouldn't more than give them a slight shock!

Now we can go back to the analogy between plants and children with a new light shed on the discussion. You cannot make an artist out of a boy who cannot draw a straight line, we have agreed. Why not? Because, if he has no tendency that way and no ability that way, it is certain either that there is no artistic bent in his more recent hereditary line or else that, when that heredity was recombined with the heredity of another family — as in the mother's or the father's — your boy received bequests from other hereditary characteristics and the art-germ was omitted, or almost so. There are artists, on both sides, who have children with no tendency that way, though that is unusual. If it occurs it means that the boy got his characteristics from those members of the line before him that were clerks or clergymen or lawyers or business men or farmers or artisans, and that the æsthetic germ somehow contrived to come to him dormant or slightly or not at all.

Heredity and environment, as a matter of fact, are the two forces that are continually striving for the mastery in the plant or the animal or the human being. If the heredity is the stronger the environmental influences will have to be increased in power tremendously to overcome the more static force that is in the heredity. Environment is galvanic, active, positive; heredity is fixed, established, conservative — in this comparative sense, it is negative. There are many cases, both in my work and in life all about me, where heredity and environment appear to be equally powerful; when that occurs you have to stand back out of the way before the collision, because it will be like that of two locomotives — the irresistible force hitting the immovable post! The splinters fly in every direction and the innocent by-stander is the most likely victim!

In animal breeding or in the development of plant life we start early and, as the experiment proceeds, remorselessly destroy the individuals that do not measure up. In human beings we cannot do that. If we could our heredity problem would be attacked first, of course through selection, then through breeding on a scientific basis, then through environmental pressure to affect gradual but sure improvement. As it is, the only thing we can hope for is to educate our young people to careful and high-minded choice of mates, then to begin to give their children environments that will discourage and thwart bad tendencies, foster and emphasize good ones, and add entirely new ones that point in the direction we want them to go, even though, in one generation, or two or six, we cannot make very rapid progress. And it is in the hope that this fundamental programme will cause you to think a little that I am writing so at length.

I have been discussing the subject thus far on the premise that the human plants in our nursery are normally intelligent, normally healthy children. Such children, reared in normal homes, and especially such as are brought up in touch with Nature — in the country or the suburbs or the small town — are not a great problem to the race. We are fortunate in America in having a vast majority of our children situated in some such environment, and even in our great cities the children of the middle classes and of the well-to-do have something of Nature brought to them in parks and playgrounds, though these are a bad substitute, in my opinion, for glades and hills and rivers and forests and the plains.

However, we have a pretty good natural environment for most of our children, if we will take advantage of it; what we must discuss for a moment now are the children whose environment is bad, worse or worst, and the children in the whole list who are below normal or abnormal.

One of the greatest fallacies of near-science and of amateurs in Nature's school is the belief that only from the normal can we get our best development and results. As a matter of fact Nature shows us again and again that it is from abnormalities that some of our most valuable and beautiful plants arise. Perhaps the very load and burden of great possibilities occurring by a chance recombination of heredities in a plant, leaves it little room for the characteristics most useful to its own continued existence. From that weak or abnormal plant — that genius-plant — may come the very characteristics we are looking for, and our only problem is to nurse it physically and keep it strong enough to pass on its overload of spiritual or æsthetic essences to its children.

How many of our great men have either sprung from weak or below-normal mothers or fathers; how many have themselves been crippled or deficient in some physical attribute? The list is long and impressive — more than that, it is sublimely inspiring! Physical defects or abnormalities may be due to the fact that the strength of the body has gone into a great soul or spirit or mind. I would be the last to condemn the weak or sickly or crippled; I have found too many cases where the physically subnormal or abnormal plant produced the finest and longest forward step in an experiment!

In the human plant, however, there is a power that my flowers and trees do not have, except in a figurative sense — the power of mentality; the question of what to do where the child plant is mentally deficient is one to be answered in love and pity rather than with cold science. Yet even here there is beginning to dawn a great hope and a great promise! For science has begun to find methods by which even the mentally deficient child can be gently but patiently pressed on by an environment of sunshine and pure air and good food, and by suggestion, education, attraction and good sense until there emerges from the darkened mind a little spark of intelligence, that may be fanned into quite a flame in time. Repetition, repetition, repetition again finds itself justified as a method here. It must be self-evident that the hopelessly deficient mental person should not be allowed to jeopardize his fellows in a violent moment; it must be fully as evident that he must be restrained from jeopardizing the race by propagating his own kind. But mercy and kindliness and generous, healthful, patient care are the least we can give our little ones who, through some weakness in heredity or some accident in environment, come into the world cursed and burdened with the horror of imbecility!

It is, perhaps, idle to repeat what every right-thinking person has been saying from the beginning of time, but I cannot help making one plea for natural surroundings for your children. In this day of the automobile and the fast local train and the 'bus it is possible for perhaps eighty per cent of Americans, at least, and of Canadians and Australians, for example, to live out where Nature is not a complete stranger to the child. Pictures of little children in the great cities in the heat and deadly fumes of summer or the bleak and deadly grip of winter so wring my heart that I cannot look at them. Stories of their transports of joy when some kind-hearted person or agency gives them a week in the country would be sufficient, if I were the tyrant and supreme dictator of the land, to cause me to raze all our large cities to the ground and send the inhabitants packing into the open! Our so-called civilization seems to be tending the other way — away from the country and toward the city.

But as I have observed in another place this growth of urban population has been given a temporary and salutary check, even though it is but a compromise, by the development of suburban living. Why are you remaining, with your child or your little brood, in the fetid and menacing atmosphere of your city, where not only the life of your child is risked daily, through accident or disease, but where the peril from bad associations is fully as menacing and deadly in the end? If it is because you cannot live elsewhere, you are to be pitied, but not blamed or censured. But is it, in fact, only because you can sleep an hour later, can find a picture show nearer at hand, can show off more to neighbors, can live a fatter or easier or softer life yourself, without sacrifice or personal inconvenience? If you are rearing little children in a city for such reasons, you are unworthy of parenthood and should be excoriated and shamed by the whole race!

Children are as much entitled to open air, to open

places, to acquaintance with Nature and her wonders, as they are entitled to justice and love and a fair chance. A child should intimately know rain and wind, grass and tree, gnats, butterflies, toads, tadpoles, birds and their nests, flowers and their haunts, hay-fields and meadows, haystacks and cellar doors, rain-barrels and the attics of barns during stormy days; they should have rabbits and chickens and squirrels and dogs for their companions and friends; they should be acquainted with dog-fennel and sassafras, they should dig caves and explore forests and sail the ocean of a mill-pond in the galley of a soap-box raft; they should be out where every breath comes freshened and stimulating from the plain or the hills, where the sun strikes into their little bodies directly, where dew can moisten their feet and snow fall on their glowing faces and the wind lift and rumple their hair!

And lastly let me say that America and Canada and Australia, among other places, but particularly and peculiarly America, is blest beyond all nations in history by another fact that comes to me immediately from Nature's school: the fact of the mixture here of all the races under the sun. I have referred to this fact before, but in this paper on the children I must remind you of the marvelous possibilities for good and evil that lie in the circumstance that here is found what Zangwill so unforgettably named 'The Melting-Pot of the World'!

The possibilities for evil lie in the natural law, observable in all Nature and observed by me intimately for seventy years in my greenhouses and gardens and on my experiment farms, that heredity

in recombination multiplies tendencies as surely as
it divides or adds or subtracts them, and that the
mingling of bad characteristics in one individual
with other bad characteristics in another will almost
certainly result in an intensification of the bad traits
of both sides. The great number of races represented
here in America, and constantly fusing through marriage, has infinite possibilities for harm and danger
to the nation; education and training and example
will help to strengthen the good in our immigrants
and newer peoples, but nothing can prevent bad results of the vicious traits and old bad influences if
old heredities are mingled and intensified by union
and reproduction.

You can cross the bad with the average or the bad
with the good and, out of the whole number of resultant individuals will come perhaps many average
and a few good ones. But when you join bad with
bad the best you can hope for is one, maybe, with
the saving spark of a few good habits from the parents (since there is no such thing as a wholly bad
man or woman!) — and the rest preponderantly
bad and perhaps a great deal worse than either of the
parents.

On the other hand, as I have suggested above, the
union of the less desirable with those who are better,
morally and mentally, will start a slow upward tendency in the family line; the corollary of the proposition is that from the joining of the best you will
get something good and worthy and perhaps something vastly superior. As in plants and animals,
so in humans: this combination and recombination
of heredities sets up a great commotion in the hered-

itary germ; the sparks fly, the whole body is thrown out of equilibrium, and from the perfected unions of germs may come the most amazing and the most attractive and desirable results.

That is why America, made up of all these combinations of races and heredities and types and varieties of individuals, has for *its national heredity*, as a whole, the sum of all the heredities of all, with the environments of all times, all peoples, all countries, all conditions, all stations, all persuasions and possibilities and potentialities. That is why America is producing now and will continue to produce versatile, adaptable, energetic, ambitious, and enthusiastic young men and women, capable of almost infinite achievements, and so constituted as to offer promise of triumphs in science and art and commerce and thought that make one dizzy to contemplate.

There is nothing magical or fortuitous in the fact that America is a great nation — very great in every sense when its youth is considered. Nature provides all the machinery and ages ago gave us all the laws. A few discerning men, like Pitt, in England, saw this before it became a fact. It could have been foretold by any naturalist, and was foretold by Emerson and Thoreau and Whitman. The joining of diversified heredities had to produce something strong, virile, adaptable. The environment of early hardship and trial, of freedom, mental and physical, of strong moral inclinations, and of incredible possibilities and natural advantages had to press on those heredities with a favorable upward tendency. There was no escaping the law!

What are we going to write on the white pages of our children's lives? For you may be well assured that it is we who must start their story for them. We must write the first paragraphs. And we must even lay out for them, up to a certain point, the plot and nature of the tale, for it is from their beginnings, given them by us, in their earliest childhood and in their schools, that they will take the leanings and the inspiration; we will influence them so that on us depends whether their narrative be petty, futile, sensational, or inspiring, uplifting, and imperishable!

XXI

WHEN the sun begins to cast longer shadows, the days to grow shorter, and the nights to lengthen and turn cooler, we in California experience a brief return of summer. It is as though the year paused a moment on the threshold of the rainy season and turned back to look somewhat longingly at its rich and fruitful months of blossom and activity and growth, a little loath to go.

In that second summer we gather our harvests.

Like the year, I pause now, toward the end of my allotted time, to glance backward and to gather my harvest of experience and growth and friendship and happy memory and, like the year, I find myself warm, mellow, sunshiny and kindly in all my motives and in my intent toward all mankind.

What has been my 'harvest of the years'?

In these papers I have tried to sketch lightly, and with broad strokes of my pencil, the development of my life and the progression of my work, my memories of men and events, the homely philosophy that has grown in my mind from my experiences and contacts, the lessons of Nature that have been learned through my association with that peer of all teachers, and the ripened thoughts that come to me whenever I sit down quietly to review my crowded, busy, profitable, and happy life. Now, when I have to turn my last page for you, I feel strongly moved to sum up the whole and try to see, as much for myself as for you — my friendly, patient and appreciative audience — what is the nature, extent, and value of the crops I have been gathering and spreading for your inspection.

As though they were the grains from the field, the fruits from the orchard and the flowers from the garden, bursting now with seed for another season's planting, I seem to see three kinds of crops in the barn and bin and crib and storehouse of this series of papers.

I see the harvest of work accomplished and aims achieved — and here I observe that the crop is somewhat short of what it might have been.

I see the harvested experiences and lessons that have moulded and impressed and enriched my own life, and here there is a first-class yield, and more than the sowing seemed to merit.

I see the harvest of dear friendships, happy memories, recollections of triumphs won and honors bestowed: here the storehouse floor groans and the walls bulge and the shingles on the roof have to give a little to make room, for the harvest is rich and heavy and abundant and we may even have to put on an ell or so to accommodate everything that is headed this way!

Looking backward down the seasons it is very interesting to me to observe how the last crop has increased with the first two and seems to have been a result of them. Perhaps there is some significance in this fact.

There are three goals toward which all men of ambition strive — toward wealth, power, or fame. You may think of a fourth — the goal of pure knowledge for its own sake, taking no account of the other three incentives. But I am inclined to believe that the most devoted and absorbed scientist or the most selfless thinker or scholar actually has a sub-conscious, if not a conscious, yearning for that power which is knowledge. So it may be safe to say that there are, really, only those three goals.

When I began my life-work I was definitely not interested in money or in money-making, except as a means to an end, and when I lapsed, as I did once or twice, and began to find myself a money-maker, I was compelled to execute a sharp right-about-face and get back to my original programme. I had no desire to be famous in the ordinary sense of the word, though I was actuated so strongly by an impulse to serve mankind that perhaps approbation of others was more of an incentive than I realized. I did have a great yearning to know, and it was not long before I was aware that there is no more useful key to the gates of all that this world holds for man than the key of exact knowledge.

I can remember now the keen zest I had for every sort and kind of information whether it applied directly to my work or not, and the reason I remember it so clearly of that slight, active, busy nuisance of a boy and youth I was, is because I have never lost it to this day. A library to me was a gold mine; a book was a trap skillfully baited to entice me in, head over heels! A man who knew something definitely could catch me with half a dozen words, and the great debt I owe some of the solid and substantial and learned men and women of wise years who were my father's neighbors and friends in New England can never be paid. I was not a bookworm nor a prodigy;

I was much more certainly set down by my elders as inquisitive and sometimes a bother, but I did want to know and I was unscrupulous in stealing something from any store that lay open to me and tireless (though maybe tiresome) in my anxiety to get at the plum preserves in the closets of other minds!

As a young man I had a good many hardships, that were salutary and strengthening to my will and my purpose, even though some of them may have taxed me physically more than was good, but none of those trials and difficulties weighed at all against the growing power I felt through the learning I acquired both from nature, from the conversations of the experienced and the wise, and from books. I have referred already to the fact that my own course through Nature's school brought me into close and invaluable contact with great and thoughtful and wise men and women; as my mind matured and developed I became more and more free of the honorable and delightful fellowship of those who are committed to the pursuit of knowledge.

If I have gleaned from these associations and this practice a wide and general education it is no more than natural; the friendships that are mine, the honors that have come to me, the success I have had, the reputation I have gained and the achievements of my life of work with flowers and trees are all due to my love of learning for its own sake and my habit of testing theories in practical application and of gaining from practical work the theories on which my conclusions about life are based.

Concerning the harvest of the years in work accomplished and aspirations achieved the record is

written in flowers and trees and shrubs and grains
and vines now growing and reproducing themselves
in probably every clime on this planet and in almost
every country. My very first work was intensely
practical: I saw a need for greater productivity,
finer qualities and sturdier plants, and I set to work
to collaborate with Nature on this task. I had a
secret ambition, even in those first years, that I
have mentioned to but few people, and that was an
ambition to work solely with ornamental trees. A
few of the great and majestic trees of New England,
such as the elm and the oak, as well as many that
were dear to me for their beauty and grace, promised large returns in satisfaction if they could be
duplicated in other families of trees less stately or
less lovely; when I came to California I was rav-
ished by the redwoods and California live-oaks, by
the eucalyptus, then newly come to this country
from Australia, and by the walnut.

Traveling about the countryside of Sonoma and
neighboring counties to-day, I am amazed myself
to come on old friends standing in groups or lining
entrance roads or following fences — old, old trees
that I planted with my own hands for my friends or
customers, or raised and sold to them for their own
planting. I had not realized how much time I spent
in those earlier years on the growing of trees nor how
much success I had, in this new country, in inducing others to grow them. You will notice that the
substantial, the thrifty, the worthy, and the likable
classes of people plant trees, no matter whether
they are in a new and treeless country or in one already well-planted, and that the shiftless, the tran-

sient, the careless, and the selfish are as little likely to set out sheltering trees as they are to be neat, thrifty, or good neighbors. Show me a developed town with no trees and I will show you a town to avoid as a home for your families. Go through districts where want and squalor and crime and filth are the rule and you will be lucky to find even a gaunt specimen of a tree anywhere about. This is not by chance; the planted and tended tree is as sure a sign of civilization as a revered flag or a church spire or a schoolhouse belfry, and the English, who have carried civilization to every part of their dominions scattered far and wide about the earth, plant shade trees almost before they finish their houses or start their towns!

But my dream of spending my life working at the improvement and development of finer and bigger and more beautiful shade trees was interrupted by the urge of more immediately practical needs of planters and gardeners and orchardists, and I was never able to do nearly as much as I always wanted to with trees. I brought together many varieties of walnuts in crosses and from these developed two trees that have a definite and perhaps an incalculable value to the world. A hardwood tree that will grow rapidly and in temperate climates would, in time, revolutionize the lumber industry. The American Government's newer policy of reforesting timber areas will probably perpetuate our softwood forests to supply the redwood, pine, and fir necessary to our country's needs for many generations to come, and if lumbermen can add to these old forests extensive plantings of a desirable hardwood the gain

to builders will be apparent. My Royal and Paradox walnuts, at least, appear from practical tests to
meet every requirement.

Meantime, though, my work had been more and
more concentrated on the improvement of orchard
fruits and the development of new varieties; it is a
satisfaction to me to contemplate the number of
new plums, prunes, cherries, pears, chestnuts, and
other valuable varieties that have first leafed and
blossomed and come to fruit on my farms. I have
described my methods with these members of my
big family sufficiently in these pages—the practical
results of the work may be inferred. The work has
not only brought into the orchards of the world
numerous new fruits and berries, but the lessons
learned, which were communicated, as fast as they
were proved, to the world of plant breeders and orchardists everywhere, have made possible an enormous and productive activity on the part of others.
So it has been not only new trees but new ideas and
new examples that have been found and developed
and given out.

Still from the purely practical angle some mention should be made of the work accomplished with
vegetables. When you remember that all our vegetables a hundred years ago and most of them fifty
years ago were accidental, purposeless, or incidental
developments, by selection, from wholly wild and
native plants, you can get some idea of the distance
plant breeding has gone with the vegetables daily
on your table. Man had been sharing the roots and
the green things and the vegetable fruits of the earth
with the animals for ten thousand years before he

began to study the possibilities for improvement in them; true, he had picked over his leeks and corn and celery and green, eating the best and discarding the inferior pieces, and he had used some selection in saving the seed for his next year's planting. But this selection had been casual and instinctive — probably, in a sense, æsthetic; the real improvement came so recently that some of us can remember the poor strains in use in the middle of the nineteenth century.

My beginnings as a gardener led me to give this matter a good deal of thought, and I have already recounted a few of my experiences in improving table vegetables. For twenty-five years I worked with corn and tomatoes; I had a long acquaintance with peppers, chard, artichokes, asparagus, and other members of the tribe, and I demonstrated conclusively that there is no edible root or leaf so humble or so long used that it does not offer the plant breeder an interesting and important field for research and concentration. There remains much to be done; what is more important, there are to-day, just as there have always been, an almost endless list of plants not at present thought of as edible, or as offering anything to man or beast, that can and some day will be bred and selected and improved until they will be added to the world's food supply. This sort of doctrine, preached in season and out, has been part of my job and part of my achievement.

Considered as a contribution to the material wealth of the world, my work with flowers has been least important of all, but I have said here again and again that the urge to beauty and the need for beautiful and gracious and lovely things in life is as vital a need as the urge for bread, even though it is a newer and less cultivated hereditary impulse than other appetites and cravings. It is very interesting to me to observe that beauty has been definitely listed on the stock exchanges of the world and that art and decoration and the creation of lovely things have been given seats on most of the boards of directors of the business institutions of our time. Long before this was generally true, I preached the doctrine of beauty as an asset and said that it was a need as definite in the human race as the need of clothing or the preservation of the species, though maybe not as strongly felt or quite as vital. I have preached it steadily for sixty years; perhaps I would have been 'a voice calling in the wilderness,' or would have been humored as a tiresome but well-meaning old bore, if it had not been for the fact that I was able to prove my point and demonstrate my theory from Nature and in the experiences I had with people who showed a need for my creations and developments in flowers.

In an article I once wrote on Orchids I find this note:

I have never worked with orchids, though I have studied them and grown thousands of the plants. The truth is that I could never interest myself in any but hardy or fairly hardy plants.

The reason is plain to me now, though I may not have recognized it then. I have not been plant breeding for the benefit of the rich, with their conservatories and their artificial tastes, nor for florists who make fortunes out of exotic and expensive varieties.

I have worked all my life for the people who love gardens and the beauty and utility of flowers, trees, and growing things and who grew them in the open field or garden, and who had no money to waste on extravagances or imported fads. Nurserymen and seedsmen have thought I ought to make a fortune; the reason why I did not may be guessed from this brief statement about orchids.

Yes, my harvest of the years in arduous work and in tasks boldly undertaken and patiently carried through is fairly large. There was much I wanted to do that I could find neither time nor money to undertake; there were enterprises that failed and projects that had to be abandoned; there were disappointments and disillusioning experiences; there were periods of discouragement and days of ill health that interrupted the progress of the work. But, taken as a whole, I suppose I have done my share, and it is with a good deal of satisfaction that I view the whole record as, more mellow and less impatient than when I was younger, I look back over the pages and try to sum up their contents.

As regards my own work I have long since ceased to think of it as anything more than a contribution to the whole body of knowledge and an addition, in its results and conclusions, to the technique and practice of plant development. For me it has become The Work. It still remains to be done — the most energetic and the most gifted and the most successful man could only add a little to the precious store of information and lay a board or two in the platform on which Science must stand. The horizon of plant breeding, as one of the richest and one of the least occupied of all the territories of Science, is illimitable. On it a few men have sketched vague pictures of the possibilities yet to be realized. Only a hint of what may be done has been revealed to us. It remains for the next few generations to develop and expand the discoveries and explorations and acquisitions of the pioneers, but that there lies beyond that horizon a new world of beauty, utility, wealth, and good for all mankind cannot be questioned. I myself have had a little glimpse of the Promised Land!

I have already written something about the friendships that have been mine and what they have meant to me. They came unsolicited, as all true friendships must come; they were brought to me, at my home, because I was too busy often to get away from there. And these friendships, as I have shown, were more often made and maintained through letters than through personal contacts. For every friend whom I have met and talked with, I have a dozen whose faces I should not know if they were to appear in my room at this moment, whose characters and lives and histories I can only infer from what they have written me, and whose voices I have never heard and shall never hear. Yet these have been marvelous and profitable friendships for me. And I am sure that, on both sides, there exists through them a loyalty, an understanding, an affection that could not be heightened or deepened if we were to be thrown together constantly to the end of our days.

The elaborate or formal honors that have been bestowed on me are gratifying to me, not so much

THE HARVEST OF THE YEARS 291

for themselves — for the gold medals struck, the medallions etched, the testimonials illuminated, the resolutions spread, or the headlines set up! — as for the kindly spirit made manifest in them and the gracious motive behind them. Honorary societies, states, the nation, and foreign governments have recognized my work, two colleges have given me degrees, the Government has passed an act of Congress designed to do honor to my services in horticulture, scientific bodies have voted resolutions or made me a fellow of their orders, and a considerable number of fraternal organizations, clubs, societies, and associations have presented me with honorary memberships to show their appreciation.

In one sense medals and ribbons and decorations and honorary memberships are part of the tinsel and pomp of life, and I have never worn a badge or a tag or signed 'Doctor' before my name or a string of letters behind it. Yet, in a record of the harvest of the years, I suppose such matters have their place and play their part. What it seems to me they demonstrate more than anything personal is that the service of mankind is always recognized, in one fashion or another, if the man or the woman concerned is sincere and zealous in that service. The service itself is, of course, the measure, but the honors bestowed are tokens, if they are not taken too seriously or overemphasized as to importance, that will serve with some accuracy as the scale by which that measure can be read.

And there is no use saying that any of us despise such honors. Now and then we pretend to, for purposes of public consumption, yet I notice that I myself often have occasion, when there are visitors around, to leave the safe door a little wide so that some one will see the trophies there and will insist on knowing what they are. They are always accommodated and shown the whole collection — a ream of papers and about a quart of medallions. We don't grow up entirely: I can get as much satisfaction out of a transaction like that as any boy with a sore thumb to display or any mighty warrior whose breast is hidden under a quarter of an acre of coveted medals!

In my harvest of the years I find, finally, a store of philosophy deduced from my experiences, my thoughts, my contacts, but particularly from my lessons in Nature's school. Philosophy is still a flourishing branch in our universities, but philosophical reflection grows a rarer thing day by day. We are so intent on efficiency, money-making, getting ahead, keeping abreast of the times, and all the shibboleths and fetishes of these times that we cannot find leisure to examine ourselves and each other and Nature sufficiently to draw conclusions and morals as we might well do. True, the old philosophers covered the ground pretty well — though I cannot find them agreeing on more than a few points; but it seems to me that philosophy, to be useful, should, like religion and science and knowledge, be brought up to date. Sophocles, Plato, Aristotle, Socrates, Kant, Spencer, Emerson all contributed something to our knowledge of why and whence and wherefor, but our modern day not only demands new thought and fresh vision, but makes both necessary because of changes it has brought to us in the facts and conditions of living.

What is civilization? What is idealism? Which way does our future lie? Why do we progress so slowly? After more than thirteen centuries of Mohammedanism, twenty centuries of Christianity, twenty-five centuries of Buddhism and Confucianism, and four thousand years of Hebrew religion, we are still greedy, cruel, selfish, short-sighted in our relations, and ready to go to war on almost any pretext and dissipate in a few months the savings of decades, the flower of our youth, and the friendliness that it has taken half a century to build up. After hundreds of years spent in fostering education and encouraging scientific research, we will throw all our hard-earned lessons aside in a moment of anger or of rapacity, and become savages again. Is there no hope for us, or are we to go forever, like the frog in the well, slipping back one foot for every two we gain?

If we look in the textbooks or the histories or the creeds of man we are certain to be baffled in our search for an answer, but if we go to Nature and inquire into her processes we discern more than one glimmer of light. The truth is that life is not material and that the life-stream is not a substance. Life is a force — electrical, magnetic, a quality, not a quantity; and if we start there we can understand a lot of things about man and his works and orders and processes.

This force is positive and negative, constructive and destructive, building up and pulling down, forward-moving and retrogressive — there is a pull of two powers all the time, and sometimes the upward pull is stronger and sometimes the down pull has the mastery. We get discouraged with the *material*, but

if we could think of the *force* we should see how
steadily and surely it is impelling us all toward a
better and higher and nobler destiny. The duty of
each individual is to make himself an influence on
the right side; electrons and molecules and all those
particles that physical science deals with have no
choice, but must pull or push, attract or repel according to their order; it is only man who can make
himself a tiny fragment of good influence and join
the positive and constructive element in this eternal
and necessary tug-of-war toward progress one way
and toward chaos the other.

If it were not for the tendency of strong, wise and
good men, of most of the women, and of practically
all of the little children of the world, to want to get
on the right side and make the pull an upward movement instead of a downward drag, I could well be
discouraged with civilization. If I have seemed, in
the last ten or fifteen years of my life, to be impatient
with education and religion, it has been, not because
I am naturally fault-finding or troublesome, but because those two forces have always been powerful
in the world and always will be, and their service
and influence in the struggle have not seemed to me
to have measured up to their stupendous opportunities. The religion that belittles or denies or stulti-
fies knowledge and science and the search for truth
is a false and dangerous religion, casting its vote on
the side of darkness; the education that makes a
machine of itself and turns all the steel of its children into the pins and needles of mediocrity is an
influence on the conservative and so on the reactionary side of the scale.

What is wrong with the world? Not commer-
cialism, the movies, war, sensational newspapers,
sex stories, short skirts, joy-riding, drinking, or jazz.
It is the spirit and tendency and disposition of the
human family; if we were on the right side, putting
all our puny strength on the rope and heaving together on the upward drag toward better things,
little details of conduct and little tempests of social
behavior and little fads and foibles and silly habits
would be of no more weight than the fly on the back
of the horse which leans into the collar and moves
the load! It is what we are trying to win for ourselves and the world that counts, and if an automobile, a talking machine, and a season baseball
ticket are all we care about having, those are about
all we shall get and our contribution to the whole
Enterprise of Life will be as negligible as though we
were Hottentots.

The state of civilization is not due to the length of
time we have had religions or education or science or
ideals; the present state of civilization is due to the
use we have made of those factors. Their influence
has been on the moral side, but has it always been
on the ethical side? It has been long on formula and
creed, but hasn't it fallen a little short on practice
and elbow-grease? And influence is the greatest
power and force in the world. Nature teaches us
that it is the moving, bending, impelling, directing,
determining factor in all life, for without it we
should be cells swimming in warm salt water to-day.

I believe in the immortality of influence.

It is the one sure, certain, permanent, eternal
thing we can know positively anything about. It is

in our own keeping and possession; it is ours to make what we will. It is given to us as the greatest and most potent gift of all our benefits and possibilities; we can strengthen and enlarge it by thought and study and care and the right heart, or we can dissipate and misuse it and so weaken it and ourselves and the race, that we become negative and worthless and a load on the backs of our fellows.

Your influence is your birthright and your epitaph. It can make you ephemeral, inconsequential, or it can sing through the years.

Mankind has always been compelled to recognize the infinite forces which are beyond his control — fundamental lines of energy — force — which through long æons of the past have resulted in animals, plants, and man, an evolution from the simple to the complex.

Mental evolution is the reaching of a man toward more and more freedom from outside aid and the steady growing toward a better mental and moral fiber from within himself.

Do I ignore what is generally called the spiritual nature of man? No; it is the corona, the flower of life, the fruit of which is Altruism — the desire to help ourselves and others to higher and better thoughts and actions; in other words, to a more perfect state of harmony with environment.

THE END